PERSPECTIVES

on CONSERVATION

EDITED BY HENRY JARRETT

BY *The Johns Hopkins Press*

BALTIMORE

RESOURCES FOR THE FUTURE, INC., Washington, D.C.

Resources for the Future is a nonprofit corporation for research and education to advance development, conservation, and use of natural resources,
primarily in the United States. It was established in 1952 with the co-operation of The Ford Foundation and its activities have been financed by grants
from that Foundation. The main research areas of the resident staff are
Water Resources, Energy and Mineral Resources, Land Use and Management,
Regional Studies, and Resources and National Growth. One of the major aims
of Resources for the Future is to make available the results of research by its
staff members and consultants. Unless otherwise stated, interpretations and
conclusions in RFF publications are those of the authors. The responsibility
of the organization as a whole is for selection of significant questions for study
and for competence and freedom of inquiry.

This book is one of Resources for the Future's general publications. It is
based on the papers prepared by authorities who participated in the 1958 RFF
Forum.

PERSPECTIVES ON CONSERVATION

Essays on America's Natural Resources

Essays on America's natural resources

by JOHN KENNETH GALBRAITH, ERNEST S. GRIFFITH,
LUTHER GULICK, EDWARD S. MASON,
THOMAS B. NOLAN, GILBERT F. WHITE

Bushrod W. Allin, Robert C. Cook, Harry A. Curtis,
Samuel T. Dana, Charles M. Hardin, Henry C. Hart,
Robert W. Hartley, Philip M. Hauser, Samuel P. Hays,
Joseph L. Intermaggio, Minor S. Jameson, Jr.,
Robert E. Merriam, Sigurd F. Olson, William Pincus,
Paul B. Sears, Byron T. Shaw, Abel Wolman

PUBLISHED FOR
Resources for the Future, Inc.

CONTENTS

EDITOR'S INTRODUCTION

The use and enjoyment of natural resources is everybody's concern. Enough food, clothing, materials to make things with, energy for homes, factories, and transportation, pure water, fresh air, elbow room in natural surroundings for sport or contemplation, and other resource products sustain life and make it worth living. Everyone wants enough of these good things for his own family and those who will come after. Also, at least in a democracy, the ultimate decisions on how to use resources are everybody's responsibility.

In exercising their responsibility, however, the people more often than not have to rely on specialists of various kinds. There are complex technologies of forestry, mining, oil and gas extraction, water development, and other fields that largely determine how much of a resource product is available and how it can be used. There are complicated economic factors that influence production and consumption and help determine who pays the costs and who reaps the benefits. There are other important, sometimes highly technical, considerations including those of political and social organization and population growth.

Specialist and layman are mutually dependent in the modern world and have a lot to learn from each other, particularly, it sometimes seems, in the field of resource conservation and development. In no field, certainly, is there greater need of bringing the two together.

The aim of this book, as of the Resources for the Future Forum on which it is based, is to bring expert opinion to bear upon a few resource problems of wide interest and significance. The informed section of the general public to which the essays are addressed is itself a large and diverse group, for in this age of specialization the authority in one field is the layman in another. Specifically, the book seeks to shed light on some of the resource conservation problems of the next fifty years from the vantage point of a critical review of the past fifty.

Reckoning from 1908 when Theodore Roosevelt convened the first Governors' Conference to consider resource problems, the idea of conservation has been a strong influence in the national life for half a century. The origins of the movement are much older than that. In the earlier years of Roosevelt's presidency there had been a spreading ferment and some notable accomplishments; and these, in turn, had been preceded by a chain of developments running well back into the nineteenth century. But it was at the time of the Governors' Conference that the conservation idea emerged fully and unmistakably as a conscious, widely recognized force in American thought and action. It has remained so ever since.

Nineteen hundred and fifty-eight, therefore, is a golden anniversary year. Through a happy coincidence it is also the one hundredth anniversary of the birth of Theodore Roosevelt. This is not, however, a commemorative volume of the conventional wreath-laying variety. Neither is it an exercise in historical analysis for its own sake. The main purpose is to examine the record of the past fifty years for the lessons that may contribute to the understanding and solution of present resource problems and those of the next fifty years. We are concerned here not with a chapter that has closed, but with a continuous set of dynamic developments that is still unfolding. This, after all, is the most fitting commemoration of T.R. and the other early giants of conservation, and the one they would have understood best: continued critical inquiry into the problems they saw as so important and absorbing.

William Howard Taft once remarked that conservation was such an abstruse subject that many people were for it no matter what it meant. There was, and still is, a good deal of truth in the tart joke. The essays in this book do not suggest any one best set of answers; many of the contributors, in fact, pointedly avoid any definitions of the key word. Some see the central problem in terms of the good life, some in terms of technology or economics, some from intermediate positions. Yet clearly the core of what they are talking about is something real that they can communicate to each other and to any reader willing to meet them halfway.

Perhaps when President Taft made his jaundiced observation he put his finger on a major strength as well as a minor weakness of the conservation idea. England and America have been well served by their peoples' highly developed genius for knowing when to rise above strict definitions, logic, and consistency in going about the public business. One of the costs of this pragmatic knack is that it enhances the importance—and the difficulty—of distinguishing the significant developments of the past from the trivial and transient. In using the past as a springboard for appraising the present and future, hard questions arise on all sides.

The essays in this book explore some of them. For example, what forces during the past fifty years have shaped American concepts of conservation and attitudes toward it? What have been the really important issues and trends in land and water, minerals and energy, outdoor recreation, and fish and wildlife management? How have resource development policies and programs affected the nation's economy, political life, and social structure—and vice versa? Most important of all, what guidance does the record of the past offer for the future? We shall surely need all the guidance we can get, in a period when the growth of cities, increases in total population, and continuing advances in technology will intensify or otherwise change the already familiar resource problems and doubtless bring some entirely new ones.

Few responsible persons care to give pat answers to large questions of this kind. This book offers none, nor does it attempt to be an encyclopedia in an assemblage of related fields that runs all the way from the A of aesthetics to the Z of zoology. It is intended, rather, as a modest guidepost toward better understanding of a set of complex and important problems. There are, naturally, conflicts among the interpretations and proposals of the twenty-three contributors, for they deal from a wide range of viewpoints with living questions and issues. But the sum of their essays adds up to more than a random sheaf of facts and comments. As a serious effort to help clarify an inherently confusing tangle of evidence, the book is held together by a definite pattern built around a central idea.

This pattern can be best explained, perhaps, by recalling briefly the series of public lectures and discussions at which the material in the book was first presented. The Forum consisted of six programs, held in the Assembly Hall of the Cosmos Club in Washington during the first three months of 1958.

Resources for the Future planned the series with three objectives in mind. One was to offer a forum in the nation's capital to some leading thinkers in fields concerned with resources from which they could express their critical appraisals and interpretations of conservation problems from their respective viewpoints. Another was to provide an audience of interested persons, not necessarily specialists, with a broad view of significant problems and trends in the field of resource conservation and perhaps with new insights on some of them. The third was to look forward as well as back from the anniversary year of 1958 in an effort to draw upon analysis of what has happened for some indication of future needs and problems.

The problem then was to subdivide this vast subject into sections that would be manageable but still hang together. One of several possible ways was the time-honored division by types of commodity or activity such as "forestry," "minerals," "recreation," "wilderness," etcetera. But a better way seemed that of taking a few of the most significant aspects of the whole conservation field. That is why after an introductory program that critically reviewed the historical background, there were successive programs on the role of science and technology, the place of the ultimate consumer in resource conservation, continued urban growth and its implications, problems of economics and political economy, and patterns of organization to gain conservation ends. The general pattern for each two-hour program was a principal paper dealing with the whole subject, briefer comments by two or three persons who had read the main paper in advance and could either take issue with or supplement its content, and a short period for discussion by both the participants and the audience.

In the choice of persons to give the principal papers and the comments, a well-tested method again was passed up for a less usual one that seemed to offer more promise. The most obvious course would have been to select prominent conservationists or others who have taken leading parts in conservation issues. There are many among them who can be counted on to give stimulating and enlightening papers. On the other hand, those persons who are most closely identified with conservation problems and issues are usually deeply committed to one side or another in fields where controversy appears to be one of the chief signs of vitality. The result would have been either a lopsided presentation or a series of debates requiring the nicest balancing. Furthermore, most of the leaders in the conservation area are highly articulate; their views are already widely known. So a plan was adopted by which each of the six authors of the principal papers, though deeply interested in, and familiar with, his respective conservation topic, was chosen primarily as one who would represent the scholar's breadth and detachment rather than the credo of a protagonist. In selecting the authors of the discussion papers one of the main objectives was a wide range of responsible opinion, so that identification with a special viewpoint was not necessarily a disadvantage. Nevertheless as a group the commentators, too, were marked by a scholarly attitude and an ability to see the whole picture. The professional fields of the Forum contributors included economics, geology, political science, geography, demography, public administration, and planning.

The idea of the 1958 Forum originated with Joseph L. Fisher, associate director of Resources for the Future, who also took the lead in shaping and carrying out the detailed plans. He was assisted by an informal staff group consisting of Henry P. Caulfield, Jr., Francis T. Christy, Jr., Irving K. Fox, and Henry Jarrett. Mr. Fisher and Reuben G. Gustavson, executive director of Resources for the Future, divided the job of chairing the Forum sessions.

Special guest of honor at the first program was Hermann Hagedorn, poet, biographer of the first Roosevelt, and director of the Theodore Roosevelt Centennial Commission. "Theodore Roosevelt's interest in conservation," Mr. Hagedorn said, "came out of his deep feeling for people. Conservation to him was not land, or water, or oil, or gas, or minerals; conservation was meeting the needs of people."

Horace M. Albright, chairman of the board of directors of Resources for the Future, was honor guest at the final session. Mr. Albright, a former director of the National Park Service and business executive, is a veteran conservationist of broad interests. In looking back over his forty-five years of experience in conservation, he expressed his belief that the early conservationists would not be surprised at the persistence of some of the big problems nor discouraged at the rate of progress thus far.

In retrospect, the quality and reception of the whole set of Forum programs more than justified the decision to depart from traditional arrangements. Both the selection of lecturers and the groupings of conservation subject matter made it possible to look at old problems from new angles and with fresh eyes and to relate resource conservation more closely with the country's total economy and social structure, and with world developments.

It is hoped that in their present form the essays will be as useful. However, they must speak for themselves; they are offered as a book, not as the literal record of the lectures and discussions. The papers have been edited, and some of them slightly revised by their authors. The record of discussion among speakers and their answers to questions from the audience has not been included, not through lack of some lively and informative exchanges, but because impromptu comment is one thing and a carefully wrought book is another. A partial exception has been made for the informal closing remarks of each principal speaker, which represent his only opportunity to reply to the comments of persons who had seen *his* paper in advance. These statements do not appear as such, but important passages have been inserted in the main texts or used elsewhere as footnotes.

The essays do not lend themselves to summary; as noted earlier they range too widely and are too undogmatic. What can be said here is that they attest—if further proof be needed—the pervasiveness of resource conservation problems and the potential breadth of future conservation policies. Population; technology; people's needs, standards, and preferences; economic and political behavior—all of these are no less involved than the resources themselves. To get a full view of conservation is to look, from a certain angle, at the whole of our modern civilization.

May, 1958   Henry Jarrett, EDITOR,
RESOURCES FOR THE FUTURE

I   THE FIRST FIFTY YEARS

Main Lines of Thought and Action
    ERNEST S. GRIFFITH

Pioneers and Principles
    SAMUEL T. DANA

The Changing Context of the Problems
    HENRY C. HART

The Mythology of Conservation
    SAMUEL P. HAYS

MAIN LINES OF THOUGHT AND ACTION

Ernest S. Griffith

The conservation movement did not begin in 1908; it certainly still has unfinished business in 1958—old battles, new frontiers, perennial confusions, widening horizons.

Nineteen hundred and eight was the date of the Governors' Conference, itself a great landmark. In 1908 the Inland Waterways Commission, with a maturity and prescience which could have been born only of prior experience, wrote of "mineral fuels on public lands," of "forests whose preservation is a public necessity for stream control, for timber supply, and for other purposes," of "improvements of navigation," of "floods and low waters," of "annual soil wash," of "reclamation by irrigation," of "water power . . . which should be used for the benefit of the people," of "the purification and clarification of water supply," of "means . . . for co-ordinating all such [governmental] agencies." Foreshadowing the future course of events was even a minority report of the representative of the Corps of Engineers dissenting from the recommendation of agency co-ordination!

ERNEST S. GRIFFITH has been Director of the Legislative Reference Service of the Library of Congress since 1940. Early in 1958 he announced plans to return to academic life as organizer and first head of the new School of International Service at American University. From 1935 to 1940 he was Dean of the Graduate School and Professor of Political Science at that University. An enthusiastic and notable hiker and mountain climber, he was long an official of The Wilderness Society. Mr. Griffith was born in Utica, New York, in 1896. He is a graduate of Hamilton College and of Oxford University, where he was a Rhodes Scholar.

In some uncanny measure this self-same commission identified all, or almost all, of the strands of conservation thought and action which crowded the intervening years and today furnish a still persistent agenda of unfinished business. The emphases have changed but in most essential elements 1958 is but 1908 illuminated.

Twice only in this century has conservation been a major preoccupation of our people and government: once in a rising crescendo which culminated in the Governors' Conference of 1908; once in the rebound from a depression's depths in the electric years of 1933–36. By a strange coincidence—perhaps resting in some obscure genes of the Roosevelt clan, more probably in the maturing of profound social forces, possibly in the sheer coincidence of two presidents whose earlier life had brought them into close and vivid relationship with forest and wild land—only in these two periods have our presidents dominated and dramatized the conservation scene. Between these years, and ever since, Congress and not the President has been the principal channel. The forces beating upon or expressed by Congress, the recommendations of the bureaus of the Administration to Congress, the deliberations and decisions within Congress—these, and not presidential leadership, have been the major factors in conservation policy development and change.

This does not mean that the other presidents have been without influence—and certainly not without views. But Taft was cautious; Coolidge, resistant to federal action; Harding was lax; Wilson and Truman and Eisenhower, preoccupied with other and to them more important matters. Hoover did possess a genuine interest and effectiveness in federal development of waterways, though with a mind set toward state rather than federal activity in other areas.

Hence the developments in conservation under these regimes were not developments characterized by strong and concentrated leadership. Rather they partook of the characteristic flavors of congressional policy—the gradual, persistent growth of problems; the slow but sure clarification of issues; the identification of local and national groups with economic or other stakes in solutions; the steady sharing of experience on the part of the bureaus concerned with their congressional counterparts—and finally decisions in Congress, in part the product of balance and compromise, but also in part, and probably in greater part, marking continuity in that growing recognition of the public interest which registered our growing national maturity and our growing concern with the future.

Much spade work had preceded 1908. Gifford Pinchot as Forester and later as Chief of the Forest Service, had not only become a national figure, but, what was perhaps more important, had established a personal rapport with Theodore Roosevelt which changed the course of conservation history. Presidents Harrison, Cleveland, and McKinley with WJ McGee, Frederick Newell, George Maxwell, and others, had fostered the practice of forest reservation.[1] The Land Grant Colleges had had four decades of activity in studying and stimulating creative agricultural land use, later to come to its full flowering when the disaster of used-up land was dramatized in the 1930's. Irrigation had made notable strides. Science and the idea of progress were twin factors in preparing the public for efficient utilization of all resources. Exposures of misuse and malfeasance had lowered the resistance potential of those who would block the public interest. The Spanish War had excited a growing nationalism, and an incipient imperialism captured the imagination of more than merely the flamboyant.

The age found the man. It is currently fashionable in academic circles to belittle the achievements of Theodore Roosevelt. Most historians would now downgrade him to the ranks of the mere near-great. No longer does the monument of Mount Rushmore with its Washington, Jefferson, Lincoln, *and* Roosevelt represent even the popular verdict, not to mention the considered judgment of our scholarly elite. The glamor of the other, later, Roosevelt, with his hospitality to ideas and eggheads, the world stage on which he played his part; the scholarly leadership of Woodrow Wilson; the political drama of Andrew Jackson; even the achievements of a Polk are preferred. Yet

[1] WJ McGee (he never used periods or separated the initials) had served under Major J. W. Powell from 1893 to 1902 as Ethnologist in Charge in the Bureau of American Ethnology. He is especially remembered for his work as a member, and secretary, of the Inland Waterways Commission, and for the study of United States water resources which he directed for the Department of Agriculture. Frederick Newell, Director of the Reclamation Service, 1907–14, was also a commissioner of the Inland Waterways Commission. George Maxwell's activities in organizing the National Reclamation Association in 1899 had led to passage of the National Reclamation Act in 1902. Subsequently, in Arizona, he organized the first Water Users Association.

there are values and a type of greatness which a scholarly icicle can never know; there is a type of leadership which a detached positivist can altogether miss. The greatness of Theodore Roosevelt lay, not in a list of specific administrative acts, or a catalogue of laws enacted under his sponsorship, substantial though both of these were. His greatness was a kind of *sursum corda,* the activating of a nation's conscience, the dramatizing of a nation's unfinished business, the energizing of much of the moral public leadership of his day—and of the next fifty years—by the impact of his personality. Harold Ickes, Henry Stimson, Charles Evans Hughes, yes, even Franklin Roosevelt, have given generous credit to this dynamic of their formative years.

In no field was this more true than in that of conservation. The drama of the rape of the forest; the epic of our waterways; the development for all our people, and not the favored few, of a new empire of land and minerals; the saga of the strenuous outdoor life—these entered into the consciousness and conscience of our people in Theodore Roosevelt's stirring years. I remember these years vividly, and what they meant to those of us who were looking for idealism in public life. From others, above all from Gifford Pinchot, came the necessary expertise, then and later; to others was left the task of development, the detail of administration. Theodore Roosevelt's role was largely of another kind—the impress once and for all on our literature, our press, our public platform, our study, our *mores,* of certain values in land, water, forest, wildlife, never again to be lost.

Taft did not so much falter as pause—pausing better to understand, more adequately to appraise, what steps should next be taken. The temper and tempo of Taft were not for Pinchot, and the latter had to go. But the circumstances of his going were not the least of the factors in keeping alive the intent of Roosevelt, and alerting President Taft himself to the dangers and intrigues of special interests. Constitutional questions of the spirit and the letter remained to be clarified, for many years to come. The forests which Roosevelt had reserved against those whom he saw as predators stalking behind the Agricultural Bill of 1907, these had to be developed—but with a wider clientele and a far longer time dimension.

It was now the turn of Congress and the states to move into the picture. Following the national impetus, forty states created conservation commissions, albeit many of them abortive. From the experience of the West came the Enlarged Homestead Act of 1909. Under legislative safeguards and administrative oversight the traditional 160-acre limitation was raised to 320 for nonirrigable lands, but with continuity of intent. The Withdrawal Act of 1910 looked in two directions. The still dynamic stand of conservation broadened and firmed the President's authority over water power and irrigation and mineral lands, and this was natural. At the same time the pressure from and experience of a West impatient with what seemed to some the arrested development of its lumber and grazing interests accompanying the policy of forest withdrawal, expressed itself in the working out of policies which, while defensible, were more acceptable to local interests.

These two strands—national planning and foresight on the one hand, and local economic interests on the other—were never thereafter to leave the arena of conservation legislation. It would be a mistake to regard these as opposites—the one wholly good, the other wholly bad. On the vitality and energy of local points of view and interests is built much of the rich tapestry of our political and economic pluralism; in the blind identification of each and every nation wide move with the long-range public interest lie dangers of centralism and neglect of secondary and derivative effects. So it is with conservation. In the long run, the development of our resources by local interests gives such development a much needed dynamic and adaptation; safeguards in long-time national interest are, fortunately, not too often incompatible with this.

Such coincidence found significant expression in the Weeks Act of 1911. Watersheds and forests of navigable streams were extended protection. Private as well as public lands were included. The pattern of federal-state co-operative action, under the stimulus of grants-in-aid, was precedent to later activities under the same act and, perhaps an even greater achievement, national forests were extended by purchase, especially in the states along the eastern seaboard. Pinchot was influential in this, as was Joseph Holmes, State Geologist of North Carolina, who in 1910 became the first Director of the United States Bureau of Mines.

From 1911 till 1920 not too much is recorded in the way of legislation. A notable exception was the establishment of the National
Park Service in 1916, a consolidation of a number of earlier, separate
establishments. These were years in which details of use were worked
out, especially in the administration of the forests. Questions of rentals
and charges were serious matters to those locally involved, but raised
little national interest. In 1912, at the behest of Stimson, Taft vetoed
a bill that did not provide for such charges. He let others go through.
One of a series of alleviations of reclamation repayments took place
in 1914. From the West, with support from Secretary of the Interior
Richard A. Ballinger, had come a move to give back to the states the
right to develop water power and control the utilization of mineral
resources; but a decision of the Supreme Court (Utah Power and
Light Co. *v.* U.S., 243 U.S. 389) in 1917 upheld the paramountcy of
the federal government in its control of water resources on public
lands. The states actually had been or were largely placated by grants
of a percentage of the receipts from forest charges and (in the case of
mineral leases) assignment of a percentage to the reclamation fund.
In general, during these years, conflicting interests had to be compro-
mised, varying methods of utilization tried, policies and standards
defined.

Again national and regional agitation played an important role.
The Hoover Dam project appeared on the horizon. The dam itself was
not actually authorized till 1928. Both in its inception and in its execution it marks the high point of Hoover's resource accomplishment.
Certain other solid accomplishments in navigation and flood control
of the Hoover presidency date from his planning during his years as
Secretary of Commerce. Incidentally, he continued such water resource planning during his presidency, and much of the later development of the Grand Coulee and Central Valley may be traced to this.
In 1913 the National Conservation Congress, in spite of efforts by
private power interests, found itself in the hands of the conservationists by overwhelming majorities. Yet by 1916 the private power interests were again in the ascendancy. The years from then until 1920
were so dominated by the war that water power legislation, such as
it was, remained pretty much of a bewildering maze, with no clear
lead. Not until 1920 was any comprehensive and clear adjustment of

the public-private power struggle to find its way to the statute books. On the forest front the public interest issue continued with champions old and new. The year 1919 saw agitation on the part of Graves [2] and Pinchot for legislation providing for public regulation of private cutting, eventually to influence the Clarke-McNary Act of 1924, and also a factor not without influence later, perhaps, in the "tree farm" movement of the 1940's among the more enlightened of the private operators.

Speculator and homesteader had for decades struggled to win points in land laws and their administration. Two laws of some consequence were passed during this period: the Agricultural Entry Act of 1914 and the Stock Raising Homestead Act of 1916. Yet the days of abundant and productive land for the taking were over; the frontier was closed. For many years the number of new homesteaders had been dwindling, and these belated attempts could not disguise or postpone the fact that new issues and new forces were paramount. New irrigation projects still had many years ahead of them, and to these homesteaders could still migrate—but for a price. How to use and lease the public lands; how to conserve the private lands; whether to confirm the lessees as owners—these were the issues of the future.

Nineteen hundred and twenty was an important year in the conservation movement. It marked the passage of both the Federal Water Power Act and the Mineral Leasing Act. The war was over; the issues had been churning around long enough, and the time had come in these two areas for a national policy to emerge. It was in Congress and not the White House that the effective maturing of decisions took place.

Mining entry had developed abuses. The lease seemed an appropriate answer, at least for the nonmetallic minerals. The act itself was a compromise between the strict conservationist views and excessive advantages for private developments. For coal, sodium, and phosphate deposits, competitive bidding was introduced. For oil and gas, prospecting rights were limited to 2,560 acres and two years. Discov-

[2] Henry S. Graves, formerly a consulting forester in partnership with Gifford Pinchot and, in 1900, founder of the Yale Forest School, succeeded Pinchot as Chief Forester in 1910. In later days he is remembered as Dean of the Yale School of Forestry.

ery gave a twenty-year lease, subject to royalties and annual rent.

Withdrawal of mineral lands in the interest of national defense had been an allowed policy for many years. The right to lease was vested in the Secretary of the Interior, however; and safeguards were inadequate unless intent of public interest were present. Nineteen hundred and twenty-one and the new Harding Administration witnessed one of the most flagrant betrayals of the public interest for private gain in our history in the Teapot Dome scandal. There is no point in recounting the episode here. It is enough to indicate the danger of postwar reaction in the conservation field, as elsewhere; but likewise to indicate the strength of public recoil that followed exposure. Conservation in the public interest may even in this case have registered a net gain.

The Federal Water Power Act was a landmark. For its day and age —a period of decline in the national ethos, of renewed predatory capitalism—it represented a real achievement. It was the end of uncertainty, the beginning of policy. Private and public interests were recognized—but the paramountcy of the national domain was established. Public charges for private power became henceforth the rule.

The next important act—and almost the only important act till the conservation explosion of Franklin Roosevelt's first term—was the Clarke-McNary Act of 1924. Here as in the Federal Water Power Act there was a crystallization of issues, a forward move with most major forces in substantial agreement. Federal, state, and private interests found therein a basis for three-way co-operation in fire fighting. Reforestation was authorized on an unprecedented scale—in fact as a program. Provision was made for the further extension of national forests, especially when watershed values were at stake. Experiment stations were established. This was followed in 1928 by the McNary-McSweeney Act which gave a statutory base to forest research. All in all, our national forest policy had largely come of age. Henceforth its battles were to be largely administrative, or those that arose out of defending a status quo against encroachment. Perhaps the only really new and major strand subsequently to appear on the forest front lay in the growing realization that the stake of the city man in the forest was not merely the forest's role in conservation, but its facilities for his future recreation. But of this more later.

The consolidation of policy in water power and forests reveals a characteristic of the conservation movement in periods of "low temperature." Except under circumstances of unique and strong national leadership—and there have been only two such in our history in this field—the over-all view is rarely taken, either by Congress or by the public generally. It is true that a considerable measure of interest arose as a result of the earlier "Conservation Congresses" and the more recent large-scale conference on "Resources for the Future." Advocates have been energized, scholars stimulated to research; the over-all and integrated view has made at least some impression upon those who generated policy in the several segments. Yet the problems of resources remain segmented, and the institutionalization of the multiple-purpose approach has been extraordinarily difficult. The Tennessee Valley Authority remains a lonely experiment.

In general, fragmentation has been the prevailing mood. Power and forests will serve as examples. In Congress today three great committees, Agriculture, Interior and Insular Affairs, and Public Works, have carved out for themselves major sectors of the resource problem. Each, especially Interior, is fragmented by subcommittees. Even this measure of consolidation represents an improvement over the splintering that existed prior to 1947. Nowhere in Congress is there an over-all, integrated view.

A similar split rules in the Executive Branch. In fact, if you read the hearings and the history of the Commission on the Reorganization of Congress you will recognize that the basic reason for establishing these three committees, in 1946, was to match their administrative counterparts—the Department of Agriculture, the Department of the Interior, and the Army Engineer Corps. These departments and the bureaus thereunder, the committees of Congress and the subcommittees therein, each have their respective clienteles in the electorates. These clienteles are fragmented. The relationships between the subcommittees or the committees and the corresponding bureaus and departments are extremely close. In fact, one might almost call them fellow conspirators along with their clienteles, rather than in any sense enemies. They are fellow conspirators not only against rival users, but also against the Bureau of the Budget, against the Appropriations

Committees, against the Executive Office as a whole, against Congress as a whole—but not conspirators against each other under normal circumstances. The fragmentation has a deeper meaning than merely the fragmentation in the Executive Branch or the fragmentation in Congress. It is a fragmentation of clienteles whose separate needs and separate pressures have resulted in the creation first of laws, and then of bureaus through the laws, to give effect to their respective policies.

Yet from time to time a national policy even in a substantial sector does in fact emerge out of conflict, experience, research, and discussion. It is this which characterizes periods of Congressional ascendancy such as the era from 1920 to 1933. In minor matters, administrative and legislative, local or special interests may prevail; in the great landmarks in forest, power, land, river development, mines, the public interest has usually prevailed—but it has prevailed in great measure by taking into account the vitality and the social contribution of the private interests.

The strength of the public and national aspects of the conservation movement was tested more than once in these years. Hoover, for example, announced a plan to transfer grazing and some forest lands to the states. The plan was killed by Congress in 1931–32. The West itself was divided. The bill for the Hoover Dam was signed in 1928, in spite of the opposition of private power interests. These had been able to delay the project, but not permanently block it. The Muscle Shoals resolution of 1931 affirmed the principle of public ownership.

Yet there was no real foreshadowing of the rebirth of conservation that was to mark the middle thirties. In retrospect one can see the forces gathering, not the least influential being the frustrations of the depression, the illogic of a system of unco-ordinated individual enterprise that left millions stranded in unemployment, that foreclosed farms, that made a mockery of the unregulated land use of a heedless age.

Franklin Delano Roosevelt had been chairman of the Committee on Forestry in the New York State Senate. During these years, he was greatly influenced by Gifford Pinchot, whose forest protection bill he introduced in 1912. Pinchot had dramatized to Roosevelt the need for forests to preserve watersheds and the land from erosion. Roosevelt had thought in terms of conservation on his Hyde Park estate.

As Governor he had appointed (and listened to) vigorous conservation commissioners in the persons of Alexander Macdonald and Henry Morgenthau, Jr. Over his young manhood had fallen the image and the dream of the other Roosevelt whom some day it would be his challenge to excel—and not the least in the field of conservation which the older man had made peculiarly his own.

Perhaps never was there a president so temperamentally receptive to new ideas. Nor, with Henry A. Wallace and Harold Ickes as Secretaries of Agriculture and of Interior, and other men of the same mood and mold as advisers and administrators, were new ideas lacking. The spectacular and abortive action of the original industrial and agricultural programs for the most part overshadowed at the time the finer, ultimately more far-reaching elements of resource planning. It was this dimension of planning and of foresight that was to come into its own. Down the great river to the gulf had gone millions on millions of tons of our best topsoil. Once rich grazing lands were starved and dust-blown, and the cattle and owners with them. Thus the Soil Erosion Service of 1933 became the Soil Conservation Service of 1935—and a program of national guidance and stimulation of wise private soils use and replenishment has been part of American policy ever since. That which began as terrace and check dams, contour and strip farming, has attained the stature of a national land policy, the child of the union of science and conscience. So also the Agricultural Adjustment Act of 1933 with its crash program matured into the act of 1938 with its "ever normal granary," its conservation overtones— and its basic attempt permanently to give the farmer economic protection.

Although at the time it was thought of only as a stopgap, the Taylor Grazing Act of 1934 through its persistence down to the present day did for the unclassified public lands much of what the Clarke-McNary Act did for forests and the Federal Water Power Act for the waters. It crystallized into policy the strands of land classification, local use and adaptation, and the conservation interests of the future. While the administration has been by no means perfect, yet what has proved to be a fundamental policy was laid down, a norm to guide alike the Administration and the local committees. In 1935, all the remaining public domain was withdrawn from entry for classification purposes.

Relatively little was subsequently released for homesteading, which, except for Alaska, may be regarded as an era that has passed.

By no means the least important part of the Roosevelt program was the famous Civilian Conservation Corps. It was a conservation of manhood, as well as of soils and forests. The sight or demonstration of hundreds of thousands of our young men engaged in conservation practices was itself an educator and dramatizer of conservation values and objectives on an unprecedented scale. The Civilian Conservation Corps has passed into history, but if this nation ever again sustains a prolonged depression, we may be certain that something of this kind will again be formed. Its limitations and shortcomings were many, but its achievements were many also—and not the least of these was in bringing to the land and forest those who never had known surroundings other than the streets and alleys of our great cities.

But the great note of the second Roosevelt era was the concept of planning. The year 1933 brought the Tennessee Valley Authority, which established the river basin in our national consciousness as a natural unit for comprehensive multiple-purpose development. The nation has never been united on questions of public power; but that a river valley has an essential unity, that its waters must serve many balanced purposes the planning of which requires foresight, that its watersheds must be preserved, its soils used wisely—these matters are no longer in dispute. They have entered into our national policy —and power, irrigation, flood control, recreation, navigation, avoidance of pollution, industrial use, watershed management have become accepted as necessary interrelated ingredients in any scientifically developed river basin. For this the TVA must take a large share of the credit. The special interests and clienteles and their bureaus may operate—or desire to operate—much as before, but their symbols must be those just mentioned. This, if it does nothing else, furnishes a platform for criticism of projects.

In 1934 the National Resources Board was established [3]—a vast, over-all concept which was a bit too far ahead of its day and age to

[3] 1935, National Resources Committee; 1939, National Resources Planning Board.

survive the perhaps inevitable reaction. Its successor was abolished by legislative action in 1943.

Other acts applying to various sectors followed shortly. The Bituminous Coal Act of 1935 and the Connally Act of the same year were more in the National Recovery Administration mood—the self-regulation of a separate industry which sought a protected or favored place in the capitalist order, free from the rigors of unrestricted competition. It will be recalled that one of the permanent—and to many, the least fortunate—aspects of the spate of New Deal legislation was the extent to which the intervention of government in the economic struggle was sought so as to give one group after another the opportunity to obtain the alleged benefits of limitations on competition and even of cartelization—though usually called by other names. The NRA codes were to a considerable extent of this character. So were the "fair practice" laws in retail trade, the marketing agreement authorizations in milk, the induced scarcity and parity legislation of basic agricultural crops, the collective bargaining and minimum wage laws in the field of labor, and certain single-industry laws of the character of the Connally Act for petroleum and the Bituminous Coal Act. Many of these were harnessed to socially desirable goals—the preservation of the soil and the family farm, the orderly use of basic mineral resources, raising the standard of living and purchasing power of labor, and other values, real and alleged. Yet in the end what emerged —in the resources field no less than in other fields—was a type of mixed, regulated, and even rigid economy quite different from the orthodox picture of a competitive, anti-monopolistic capitalism. The fact that government regulation was to some extent substituted for the privately administered price may or may not have been a long-run asset. The role of government itself—in resources, as well as elsewhere—was basically transformed in the popular mind from that of a policeman to that of a weapon in the economic struggle. Henceforward, business, labor, agriculture and the professions alike (and not merely the industries sheltered by a protective tariff) came to look to government for both defensive and offensive intervention in most of the major sectors of what had become a *political* economy.

Two other acts deserve notice in this period. The Flood Control Act of 1936 was particularly extensive, and also incorporated principles of local contributions and maintenance. The Norris-Doxey Act of 1937 expanded technical advisory services to privately owned forests and also encouraged tree planting, especially in shelter belts.

Nonmaterial values also emerged in the general national awakening of these recovery years. The Civilian Conservation Corps and the Tennessee Valley Authority had evangelical overtones among their economic objectives; but other moves, chiefly administrative, were more clearly inspired by the recreation needs of the present and future, and even by a nostalgia for the age of the hunter and pioneer. Wildlife and game refuges had begun to appear soon after the turn of the century. The first Federal Wildlife Conference was held in 1936, to be followed by the institution of a national system of wildlife refuges in 1937. The Pitman-Robertson Act, the Duck Stamp Act, the international migratory bird treaties were all products of this strand. Stimulated by Aldo Leopold, the Gila Wilderness Area had been established as early as 1924. In 1935, Robert Marshall and others launched The Wilderness Society.[4] This was designed to salvage for future generations some at least of the few remaining primitive wilderness areas. The United States Forest Service instituted protective regulations on its wilderness and wild areas in 1929. Meanwhile the National Park System surged forward, with its acreage growing from 4,821,760 acres in 1916 to 15,253,535 acres in 1936 and to 24,-397,985 acres in 1956. Some of this growth was by legislation; some (in the shape of "national monuments") by executive orders. Conservation consciously and rationally was acquiring a new dimension —actually one which it had never been without, at least emotionally, from the days of that great naturalist John Muir. It was given new

---

[4] Aldo Leopold and Robert Marshall were both active in organizing The Wilderness Society. Both for many years had served with the United States Forest Service. Leopold joined the Service in 1909, and in 1924, when Assistant District Forester in Charge of Operations, entered private consultancy practice; from 1933 to 1948, when he died, he was Professor of Wildlife Management at the University of Wisconsin, and it was during this period that he produced most of his writings on wilderness areas. Marshall had joined the staff of the Forest Service in 1924; from 1933 to 1937 he was Director of Forestry of the Office of Indian Affairs, and from 1937 to 1939, when he died, he was again with the Forest Service as Chief of the Division of Recreation and Lands. It was under his leadership that the system of wilderness areas in Indian reserves and national forests was created.

urgency by the necessity of balancing values under a now obvious population pressure. Much of this approach had previously crystallized in New York State where, by constitutional amendment in 1894, its forest preserve was to be kept "forever wild." The Adirondacks and the Catskills to this day reflect the continuing and broadened popular support of this policy. More recently, Maine, California, and Michigan have joined New York in recognizing the values of primitive wilderness; while a whole procession of states has undertaken the development of systems of state parks for various types of outdoor recreation.

The shadow and eventually the substance of the Great War directed the nation's attention to its growing scarcities, and at its end added uranium and atomic materials to the category of basic resources. Agriculture resumed its expansion as the bread basket for much of the free world. The use of oil was stepped up enormously. Some thought they saw clearly the often proclaimed but elusive end of domestic oil production by the usual drilling. We are now more fully aware that the precise date was and is debatable. Nineteen hundred and forty-four saw a response to this threat in the passage of the Synthetic Liquid Fuels Act, which authorized demonstration projects of the feasibility of use of oil shale, of which we possessed enormous quantities. However, private exploration and development of alternative foreign sources was the more immediate effective response in petroleum, and also in iron ore and strategic metals generally. Defense stockpiling and exploration under the auspices of the Munitions Board prior to World War II had brought but meagre results. The National Security Resources Board of 1947 and its successors instituted long-range programs of stockpiling and planning under the aegis of national defense. The first atomic energy act was passed in 1946—largely to establish an institutional base for further policy development. Efforts to amend the write-off tax provisions of our mining and drilling interests in favor of the general taxpayer were met in part by the strengths of the mining interests. However, there was also a sense that, as many of these resources became scarcer within the borders of the United States and our dependence on overseas sources grew, it was all the more important to place a premium on domestic exploration and development. Of this same character was the transfer of tideland oil to the states and by them to a more rapid private exploitation.

By 1947 it became all too clear that the Communist world was enemy and not ally. By 1950 the cold war flared into actual combat in Korea. Henceforth considerations of national defense were to influence, if not dominate, much of legislative and administrative policy. In this setting the Paley Commission produced its restrained, statesmanlike report on materials policy. It provided the best factual, scientific base yet for holding the scales between exhaustion and discovery of strategic vital materials and sources of energy.

Conservation as a movement and as a policy was reaching maturity. Intensive management, multiple use, foresight were coming into their own. The mood was obvious on many fronts.

In the whole area of water resource development, while public *vs.* private power remained a sharp political issue, the operative differences were narrowing. Whether by the aid of Madison Avenue or by a sharpened conscience or both, the private power group now accepted the premise that its tenure must be justified in terms of the public interest. On the other hand, public projects were required in Congress to justify themselves through an appropriate cost-benefit ratio, else appropriations (if not authorizations) would not be forthcoming. If "public relations" occasionally glossed over sharp practice on the part of the utilities, so too did legerdemain in bookkeeping and estimates from time to time induce Congress to accommodate local desires for construction, flood control, cheap power, or irrigation. Yet private and public alike accepted the requirement that what they did or wanted must be justified in terms of a fairly concrete national interest. As experience sharpens the tools of analysis, we may at least hope for greater conformity to public norms. Although water developments, particularly for municipal and industrial consumptive uses, will continue to rise, probably opportunities for the economically justified large-scale public hydroelectric power projects have about run out with those already authorized. The Columbia may be an exception. The battle ground of public *vs.* private power has shifted to atomic energy. Attacks by private interests on demonstrably successful public programs, such as rural electrification, have been virtually stillborn. A policy of "containment" on both the public and private fronts seems likely to prevail—with each *ipso facto* serving as a yard-stick on the other.

In forest management, also, a somewhat similar convergence has become apparent as between public and private forestry. In 1941, the "tree farm" movement was formally launched, with its philosophy that timber is a crop and its objective of sustained yield. This steadily gained adherents, especially among the larger timber interests, some of whom had earlier introduced such practices. At the same time, differentiated, intelligent use and intensive management made steady progress in the Forest Service. The findings of research as to sustained yield, watershed management, fire fighting, insect and disease control were translated into policy. The single-purpose attack on Forest Service ownership and management by certain of the private grazing interests was rebuffed in Congress. Politics continued to swirl around the Forest Service, but it was by groups which felt the need of factual justification of their case—and more and more congressional decisions (as well as those within the Service) were based on such justification.

So also in the field of minerals. One would hesitate to say that the days of spurious claims or of ruthless exploitation were over. Yet the Multiple Mineral Development Act of 1954 resolved some at least of the conflicts between mineral leasing and the general mining laws. The further revision of the mining laws in 1955 revealed additional progress in the direction of maturity—a maturity marked in this instance by the policy of safeguarding, so far as still was practicable, the vegetative surface for the public interest. Without entering into the merits of the controversy, the Al Serena case in 1956 illuminated the state of public opinion on the subject. The whole discussion centered around the merit of the mining claim. It was assumed that in the absence of such merit, the use of the valuable timber rights was totally unwarranted. At least local opinion, and probably national as well, would have winked at such an assumption not too many years ago.

Nowhere more than in recreation is it apparent that a new and powerful element has been added to resource management. Population pressures; the shortened work week; the presence of three generations of boy scouts in the community; the drama of the Civilian

Conservation Corps; the steadily mounting millions of visitors to national and state parks and forests; the expanded clientele of hunting and fishing; the interest in wildlife; the growth of a thirst for and sense of beauty, not only in art and music but in nature; a re-examination of the contribution to our national tradition, fitness, and character of the out-of-doors—these and other social forces have brought strength to nonmaterial insights and values. The "Mission 66" program of the National Park Service withstood the general cuts in estimates in 1957. The recreation wing of the conservation front was strong enough to defeat the powerfully supported Echo Park Dam in the Dinosaur National Monument in 1956. It saved, at least temporarily, the Wichita Mountains Wildlife Refuge from the designs of the Department of Defense. It is rallying support for giving a statutory base to the few remaining wilderness areas—symbols of values of past days that have their importance for present and future generations as well. We may even come to measure the maturity of a civilization by the regard it pays to nonmaterial values—in the conservation field no less than elsewhere.

Not all is well, especially in those matters which arise out of an archaic system of organizing resource decision making. Agriculture, Interior, and the Corps still have rival plans and approaches to river basin development. Their counterparts on Capitol Hill—the Agriculture, Interior, and Public Works committees—have no effective liaison. What little over-all view there is in the Executive Branch stems from a small unit in the Bureau of the Budget, and the relatively untried co-ordinator of public works planning in the White House. Structured efforts at co-ordination in the shape of river basin interdepartmental committees have registered relatively little success. In the end, perhaps only the fiscal controls in the Executive as well as in Congress may contain the answer to the crying need for more effective multiple-purpose development of land and water. For the present, rival clienteles have entrenched themselves in their institutional counterparts. Nor have Soil Conservation and Agricultural Extension reconciled their differences.

The past decade has seen some noteworthy studies by commissions. The Natural Resources Task Force of the First Hoover Commission was marked by its attention to organizational problems, and by its illumination of the influence of structure on policy. Its recommendation that a Department of Natural Resources be established has to date marked the high point in integrating thought. The Water Resources and Power Task Force of the Second Hoover Commission was most useful in its devastating attack upon the estimating and accounting practices of certain of the public agencies. Its conclusions in the direction of return to private operation got nowhere, perhaps because of the widespread, almost intuitive feeling on the part of many people that there was merit in retention (and implicit competition) of both public and private enterprise, with each type having continually to justify itself.

Mention has already been made of the Materials Policy (Paley) Commission (1952). There were also the Water Policy Commission of 1950–51 and the Cabinet Advisory Committee's Report of 1955 in the water resources field. Both alike called for a tie-in with local units; both saw problems in river basin and multiple-use terms; both called for a national board of review; but the earlier report was the stronger in terms of formulation of a national policy. It also was buttressed by elaborate research in the extent and nature of our water resources and the detail of our conflicting water laws. During these same years the House Interior and Insular Affairs Committee sponsored a number of studies co-ordinated by the Legislative Reference Service, which, though abortive in achieving their total concept, did make a considerable contribution in highlighting the potentials of ground-water management. In 1953, under Ford Foundation financing, Resources for the Future sponsored a notable conference which dramatized the many-faceted nature of the conservation problem, and set forth a program of research frontiers still to conquer. These studies and others only a degree less significant were likewise signs of our national maturity of approach.

In retrospect, it is clear that certain persistent strands have marked these fifty years in conservation. The distribution of light and shade between them has varied, but little that is actually new has entered.

There has been ever present the dilemma between future use and present consumption. It first showed itself in the plundering of the nation's forests; but these were renewable and this battle is almost won —not by locking up the forests, but by their sustained use. Next it was dramatized in the field of soils by the dust bowl and overgrazed and overused lands; and the soil conservation movement is doing its work of adjustment. It moved then into the field of minerals under the spur of defense considerations. Research, invention, chemistry, stockpiling, atomic energy, and imports have provided at least a partial answer. The dilemma between future and present today centers also around a new set of resources—wilderness, parks, wildlife—but it is the same dilemma.

Subsidiary to this has been the dilemma of the nature of present use. Shall it be exploitive or developmental; wasteful or scientific? The theoretical battle is won on this front; the political battle is still with us in isolated sectors. It was the chief dilemma in the early days, but we have come far.

The strand or dilemma of public *vs.* private ownership and development has likewise been persistent. Two values, initiative and national interest—both of them good—have provided a philosophic basis for the struggle. Yet as public instrumentalities have developed ways of greater initiative and private corporations have acquired more of a social sense, this struggle has assumed somewhat less importance. If there is to be private monopoly, it is accepted doctrine that it must be regulated. Theodore Roosevelt was not doctrinaire on the subject. He attacked monopoly and predatory private interests when they did violence to conservation ideals; he used and even welcomed private interests when they co-operated.

Always the scientific strand has persisted, and some really permanent victories seem to belong here. Commissions, research, experiment, accounting—these have laid the groundwork. To these is appeal made in Congress; by these the results are more and more judged. From these have sprung other strands—multiple use, intensive development, sustained yield, and a hundred other more detailed administrative decisions.

Present always has been a persistent political pluralism—geographic and economic. It is this pluralism that has blocked so many efforts at a national and integrated approach. On the other hand, it is geographic pluralism that has been the life blood of multiple-purpose river basin development—though often tying such development into knots of internal contradiction. Both types of pluralism have found expression in institutional counterparts, in federal bureaus with special-interest clienteles, in regional "authorities" and "administrations," in Congressional committees. Most of the abortive moves to transfer certain resource functions to the states have been largely inspired by local economic interests, though usually defended on "constitutional" grounds. Localism for many years blurred the effectiveness of national administration, as the populace and their representatives in Congress rallied to the support of those whose habitual way of making a living "regardless" was threatened by administered conservation. National planning has made headway, but at least in part as it has forced divergent local interests to face their problems together. Finally there has been the dilemma of the spiritual versus the material, perhaps never more plainly articulated than by Theodore Roosevelt, but expressing itself more intensely today as the shortcomings of urbanism become increasingly apparent.

So the history of conservation could well be written, not so much chronologically, or institutionally, but in terms of these interwoven strands. Almost never did they appear in isolation. Rather could they be identified in each and every major situation as it developed. They are all with us today, but we are a more mature people. Our hierarchy of values has been rearranged somewhat, and for the better.

Today, as in the past, individual leadership counts for much. The great leaders of the past—Pinchot, the two Roosevelts, Senator Francis G. Newlands, WJ McGee, Harold Ickes, Hugh Bennett, Morris Cooke, Senator George Norris, and others—have done their work well in educating a nation. Others are taking their place today; and their task in many respects is an easier one, for the groundwork has been laid and millions of Americans are with them in this, one of the noblest tasks to which a man may devote his life—the enlightened conservation of the natural heritage of a free people.

PIONEERS AND PRINCIPLES

✍ Samuel T. Dana

Dr. Griffith has covered the subject so admirably that I can do little except to add a few supplementary facts and thoughts.

He is to be congratulated on his wisdom in avoiding any definition of "conservation"—either his own, or someone else's. I shall follow his example. I should like, however, to indicate what I conceive to be the objective of conservation both as a philosophy and a program of action: namely, to bring about the widespread adoption of policies and practices that will promote the public interest in all matters relating to the management and utilization of natural resources.

Unfortunately, no two people completely agree on what constitutes the "public interest," no matter how meticulously it is defined. One seldom has any difficulty in convincing himself that any policy or

SAMUEL T. DANA, Dean Emeritus of the School of Natural Resources, University of Michigan, has been associated with that University since 1927, as Professor of Forestry, first Dean of the School of Forestry and Conservation, and first Dean of the School of Natural Resources. From 1907 to 1921 he was with the United States Forest Service, as forest assistant and assistant chief of silvics and forest research. He was Forest Commissioner of Maine from 1921 to 1923, and from 1923 to 1927 he was director of the Northeastern Forest Experiment Station. He has been president of the Society of American Foresters, editor-in-chief of the *Journal of Forestry,* and a director of The American Forestry Association and has frequently been a consultant to the federal government on national and international matters. Dean Dana was born in Portland, Maine, in 1883. He is a graduate of Bowdoin College and the Yale University School of Forestry.

24

action he favors is clearly in the public interest; or if, deep down in his heart, he has any doubts, he is certainly not going to confess them. This human frailty is responsible for much of the confusion and conflict that has characterized the movement throughout its history.

It may, however, help to clarify our thinking to explore a bit further some of the dilemmas to which Dr. Griffith has called attention and which have continually plagued us during the last fifty years in our efforts to identify and to promote the public interest. These dilemmas involve real or apparent conflicts between present and future, between individuals and communities, between federal and state governments, between uses and values, between extensive and intensive management, between thrift and prodigality in consumption.

Conservation as an organized movement, although not under that label, started in 1873, when the American Association for the Advancement of Science appointed a committee "to memorialize Congress and the several State legislatures upon the importance of promoting the cultivation of timber and the preservation of forests, and to recommend proper legislation for securing these objects." This action was motivated by fear of a future timber famine and by the conviction that such a famine could be averted only by governmental action. Both the fear and the conviction are implicit in the title of a paper presented before the Association by Franklin B. Hough, one of the fathers of American forestry: "On the Duty of Governments in the Preservation of Forests." To a small but far-sighted and public-spirited group of individuals it was clear that current methods of exploiting the timber resources of the country, however profitable from the private point of view, endangered the public interest—both present and future.

Since the exploitation centered chiefly in forests recently acquired from the public domain, often by questionable methods, its control clearly lay in retaining the lands in public ownership and permitting removal of the timber by private enterprise under governmental supervision. Efforts of the AAAS, The American Forestry Association, and the National Academy of Sciences to achieve this goal finally resulted in passage of the acts of 1891 and 1897 providing for the establishment and administration of forest reserves. Both acts were attached as riders to bills dealing with other subjects. Prominent among those who deserve credit for this achievement, and whose names should appear in any roster of early conservationists, were Dr. Hough, first chief of the Division of Forestry in the United States Department of Agriculture; John A. Warder, founder of The American Forestry Association; Bernhard E. Fernow, also a chief of the Division of Forestry and a leading member of The American Forestry Association; Secretary of the Interior Carl Schurz; Commissioners of the General Land Office James A. Williamson and William Andrew Jackson Sparks; Assistant Commissioner Edward A. Bowers; and Charles S. Sargent, chairman of the Forestry Commission of the National Academy of Sciences.

Dr. Fernow coupled the twin philosophies of the indispensability of *all* natural resources and of the responsibility of government for their wise use in a way that anticipated their popularization under Gifford Pinchot and Theodore Roosevelt and in the 1908 Conference of Governors. In a vice-presidential address before the AAAS in 1895 on "The Providential Functions of Government with Special Reference to Natural Resources," he made these trenchant statements: "Only those nations who develop their natural resources economically, and avoid the waste of that which they produce, can maintain their power or even secure the maintenance of their separate existence. A nation may cease to exist as well by the decay of its resources as by the extinction of its patriotic spirit. . . . Whether fertile lands are turned into deserts, forests into waste places, brooks into torrents, rivers changed from means of power and intercourse into means of destruction and desolation—these are questions which concern the material existence itself of society. . . . It is true that as individuals the knowledge of the near exhaustion of the anthracite coal-fields does not induce any of us to deny ourselves a single scuttle of coal, so as to make the coal field last for one more generation, unless this knowledge is reflected in increased price. But we can conceive that, as members of society, we may for that very purpose refuse to allow each other or the miner to waste unnecessarily. . . . Here the general principle of Roman law, *Utera tuo ne alterum noceas,* prevention of the obnoxious use of private property, establishes readily the propriety of State interference, and by *alterum* we are to understand not only the citizen of the present, but of the future as well."

Exercise of the providential function of government through the retention of public lands in public ownership started with the establishment of national parks, four of which preceded the first forest reserves (renamed national forests in 1907). These were Hot Springs in 1832, Yellowstone in 1872, and Yosemite, General Grant, and Sequoia in 1890. Since the turn of the century the system has been greatly enlarged and substantial reservations have been made of mineral lands and water-power sites. Recognition of both aesthetic and material values has long characterized the attitude of government toward its public lands.

The future of unreserved lands still remaining in the public domain is not yet clear. The Taylor Grazing Act of 1934, it must be remembered, merely authorized the establishment of grazing districts on public land "pending its final disposal." No further action has been taken by Congress, and the grazing districts are still officially classified as unreserved public domain. In addition, there are nearly 19 million acres of land in the unreserved public domain outside of grazing districts which are leased for grazing and more than 5 million acres of commercial forest land, the future of which is at best uncertain.

The apparently widespread belief that the first reserves of federal land were "locked up," and that "multiple use" is a concept of recent development, is hardly in accordance with the facts. Secretary of Agriculture James Wilson's letter of instructions to Pinchot in 1905, when the forest reserves were transferred from the Department of the Interior to the Department of Agriculture, was emphatic on these points:

> All of the resources of the reserves are for *use* [italics are in the original], and this use must be brought about in a thoroughly prompt and businesslike manner, under such conditions only as will insure the permanence of these resources. The vital importance of forest reserves to the great industries of the Western States will be largely increased in the near future by the continued steady increase in settlement and development. The permanence of the resources of the reserves is therefore indispensable to continued prosperity, and the policy of this department for their protection and use will invariably be guided by this fact, always bearing in mind that the

conservative use of these resources in no way conflicts with their permanent value.

You will see to it that the water, wood, and forage of the reserves are conserved and wisely used for the benefit of the home builder first of all, upon whom depends the best permanent use of lands and resources alike. The continued prosperity of the agricultural, lumbering, mining, and livestock interests is directly dependent upon a permanent and accessible supply of water, wood, and forage, as well as upon the present and future use of their resources under businesslike regulations, enforced with promptness, effectiveness, and common sense.

Creation of forest reserves put a stop both to trespass on them and to their acquisition by private owners at a tithe of their real value, but that it arrested the legitimate development of the lumber industry or any other industry is highly unlikely. Multiple use of the reserves for "water, wood, and forage" (as well as for minerals, the utilization of which was not under the control of the Department of Agriculture) was extended to include recreation as a growing population, automobiles, and the call of the wild steadily increased their value for this purpose. The extensive tracts set aside as "wilderness" and "wild" areas, as well as the program entitled "Operation Outdoors," testify to its importance in current administration of the national forests.

In view of the popularity that the theory of multiple use has recently attained as the key to land management in the public interest, it may be well to emphasize the fact that it is neither new nor a panacea. Its practical application immediately raises the question of what uses are to be favored, where, when, and by whom. How much water, wood, forage, minerals, wildlife, and recreation do we want, and who is to produce them? How do we compare tangible and intangible, material and spiritual values, for which there is no common measuring stick? Answers to such questions as these must be supplied in the first instance by legislators and administrators on the basis of the best information available, and in the long run by the general public whose interest it is the function of conservation to protect. Fifty years from now we shall know better than we do today how wise the judgments of these groups have been.

Decision as to what we want from our natural resources in the way of goods and services must be followed by management that will result in their actual production. This is no easy task. Very little, if any, land is physically and biologically well adapted to all uses, and different uses often conflict. No matter what the quality of the land, it cannot produce maximum amounts of everything. If we want more water or more forage, we may have to grow less timber. If we want more timber for commercial utilization, we may have to be content with less extensive parks and wilderness areas. The inspiration afforded by roadless areas will be experienced by fewer people than if they were made more accessible.

These considerations make it necessary to decide just what use or combination of uses will be favored on a particular piece of land. Much remains to be learned as to the techniques by which the desired objective can be attained. Research, which provides the tools for translating plans into action, and which received its first substantial recognition in the field of wildland management in the McSweeney-McNary Act of 1928, is consequently an essential part of the conservation program. Its urgency increases as mounting pressures on natural resources necessitate the stepping up of production through more intensive measures of management. Sustained yield which, like multiple use, has become a phrase with which to conjure, attains its greatest usefulness only as yields are sustained at higher and higher levels—a goal which requires more and more technical and managerial skill.

A related aspect of conservation which deserves more emphasis than it commonly receives is thrift in consumption. The greatest drain on natural resources comes not so much from the increase in population as from the constantly rising standard of living. During the last fifty years our consumption of nearly every product of the land has been greater than during all the previous years in our history. No one regrets that what was a luxury for the father has become a necessity for the son; but does that necessity require a prodigality in use that leads to unnecessary waste? Could we not live comfortably without burning so much gasoline in our automobiles, and without consigning so much material to the trash burner and the dump heap? Growing two trees where one grew before is no more effective in meeting our needs than is making one tree do the work of two. Science is helping greatly in this direction by developing new uses, new materials, and new processes which permit the more economical use of natural resources, but personal restraint in limiting our consumption to our real needs would constitute an important contribution to the same end, with desirable moral as well as physical results.

The final aspect of conservation on which I wish to touch is the relationship between the federal government, state governments, corporations, and individuals. The facts that the federal government was first to take positive action to protect and manage the lands which it owned, and that conflicts involving a clash between public and private interests have commonly been fought at the federal level, have tended to create the impression that Uncle Sam must play the leading role in conservation matters. Both states and private owners take vigorous exception to this point of view. These groups feel that, while they may have been slow in getting under way, they have now come of age and can manage their own affairs with a minimum of federal interference and a modicum of federal help.

A subject of continuing, and mounting, friction between the federal government and the western states is that of water rights. The states claim that acts passed in 1866, 1870, and 1872 relinquished to them whatever rights the federal government may have had to control the use of the water of non-navigable streams in the West. The Department of Justice claims that these acts made no grant to the states, but merely granted to appropriators water rights acquired under state laws. There is general agreement that Congress has control over the navigable portions of interstate streams, and the contention of the states-rights advocates that this control does not extend to non-navigable waters, or to any purpose other than navigation, has not been upheld in several Supreme Court decisions. The states are consequently seeking legislation to affirm the rights that they believe they possess.

Three cases are of special interest. In 1940, in United States *v.* Appalachian Electric Power Company, the Supreme Court held that the New River, in Virginia, is a "navigable water" in spite of the fact that obstructions currently prevent navigation, and also that federal control over navigable streams is not limited to navigation. A year later, in Oklahoma *v.* Atkinson Company, the Court went considerably further: "The fact that ends other than flood control will also be served, or that flood control may be of relatively minor importance, does not invalidate the exercise of the authority conferred on Congress. . . . It is clear that Congress may exercise its control over the non-navigable stretches of a river in order to preserve or promote commerce on the navigable portions. . . . And we now add that the power of flood control extends to the tributaries of navigable streams. . . . There is no constitutional reason why Congress cannot under the commerce power treat the watersheds as a key to flood control on navigable streams and their tributaries." Again, in 1954, in Federal Power Commission *v.* Oregon *et al.* (the "Pelton Dam case"), the Court held that the government has complete control over reserved lands in the public domain and in Indian reservations, and that it can license such lands for the development of hydroelectric power without regard to state law or to the wishes of the state. Whether federal or state control is preferable from the conservation point of view is a moot question.

A triangular relationship between the federal and state governments and private owners exists in the fields of public control over the activities of private owners and of federal grants-in-aid to the states for the encouragement of improved practices by private owners. Gifford Pinchot and his followers took the position, in the case of forest lands, that only the nation is big enough and strong enough to exercise any effective control over powerful private interests. William B. Greeley, as chief of the Forest Service, questioned the wisdom of federal control on both theoretical and practical grounds. He favored, instead, a combination of state controls and federal grants-in-aid such as those embodied in the Clarke-McNary Act of 1924, the Norris-Doxey Act of 1937 (now repealed), and the Cooperative Forest Management Act of 1950. Although several states have enacted regulatory laws, their effectiveness as a means of enforcing substantially higher standards of forest practice by private owners is open to question. In other fields, such as the control of stream pollution and the exploitation of oil and gas, the states have met with better, though by no means complete, success. Co-operation with private owners, with the help of federal grants-in-aid, is more popular than regulation and is working out reasonably well. In general, it is fair to say that within the last twenty to thirty years the states have greatly strengthened their activities in the conservation field.

During this same period progress by private owners, in voluntarily adopting improved managerial practices that can be regarded as clearly in the public interest, has been unexpectedly rapid. The Code of Fair Competition for the Lumber and Timber Products Industries, which was adopted under the short-lived National Industrial Recovery Act of 1933 and which pledged the industries "to carry out such practicable measures as may be necessary for the declared purposes of this Code in respect of conservation and sustained production of forest resources," may have had something to do with the change. So, too, as Dr. Griffith suggests, may the threat of federal control and the partial reality of state control. The principal reason, however, for improved practices by private owners—whether of forest, range, or mineral lands—is economic. Growing scarcities, higher prices, and improved technologies of harvesting and manufacturing make more intensive management a paying proposition in coin of the realm. Financial profit exercises more influence on the behavior of the private landowner as a land manager than do the police power of the state, education, and sentiment combined. Intensive management was not practiced until recently because the owner felt that he could not afford it; today it is being practiced more widely, although far from universally, with consequent promotion of the "public interest," because it pays.

Let me conclude with a summary of the salient points I have tried to make: The objective of conservation of natural resources is to promote the "public interest." Because of the many diverse, often conflicting, factors involved, that interest is difficult to identify and harder still to attain in practice. During the latter part of the last century the ground was well prepared for the flowering of the conservation movement that took place in the early 1900's. In the fifty years that have elapsed since the Governors' Conference of 1908, progress has been intermittent but on the whole reasonably steady. We have come a long way, but we still have a long way to go.

Judgments as to relative values are gradually maturing; the potentialities and limitations of multiple use, sustained yield, and intensive management are being better appreciated; research is sharpening the tools of land management and making possible greater economy in utilization. Most important of all, public agencies (both federal and state) and private owners, in spite of recurring misunderstandings and disagreements, are working together in a new spirit of co-operation. In today's economic climate, it begins to look as if the conflict between public and private interest, between present and future, might be less acute than formerly. "Planning" is no longer a dirty word.

On the other hand, the appraisal of relative values and the allocation of uses to specific pieces of land are becoming more difficult. We are still a conspicuously wasteful people, although today our prodigality is more evident in the consumption of finished products than in the harvesting of raw materials. The apparently never-ending increase in population and in standards of living raises new problems and intensifies old ones. These can be solved only by research on an ever-widening scale and by prompt and widespread application of the results. Whether progress in the next fifty years will be more substantial than in the last fifty depends on our ability to effect "the union of science and conscience," as Dr. Griffith put it, in sound policies and practices of land management.

THE CHANGING CONTEXT
OF THE PROBLEMS

Henry C. Hart

Mr. Griffith's account of fifty years of conservation has been too comprehensive, too honest with the events, to gloss over what he calls the "perennial confusions" of the story. He thus enables, indeed, I suspect tempts, his commentators to try their hands at reconciling the inconsistencies and explaining the contradictions. Conservation meant a national and integrated approach: Why have some of its best manifestations been regional, and none of them comprehensive of all resources? As a nation, we are maturing toward a general high regard for conservation values: Why is conservation (to say the least) no more continuously the subject of vigorous presidential leadership than it was a half century ago? And in the face of all the unfinished battles Mr. Griffith has reported, can we say that conservation is a *movement* now, or was a movement even at the peak of Franklin Roosevelt's leadership, in the concerted, crusading form it assumed at the time of Theodore Roosevelt?

Nature made the world Theodore Roosevelt's Americans lived in;

H E N R Y C. H A R T, Associate Professor of Political Science at the University of Wisconsin, is an alumnus of the TVA (1936–43) who has since studied river development in two other areas. The resulting books are entitled *The Dark Missouri* and *New India's Rivers*. He has been interested in the way people's demands upon their water resources affect the kinds of developments they can make work. He was born in Tennessee in 1917, and received his B.A. degree from Vanderbilt University and his Ph.D. from the University of Wisconsin.

men made ours. That is the first of the four changes of context which, if we take them into account, can help us solve these riddles. How thoroughgoing the change is we can detect at once by sampling afresh the common sense of the early 1900's as it was passed on to the young. Mark Sullivan, gathering from the memories of men and women still alive in 1927 the contents of the old-time singing geographies, recorded in *Our Times* that the state capitals were learned this way:

Maine, Augusta on the Kennebec

New Hampshire, Concord on the Merrimac . . .

But already, in 1927, he had to explain in a footnote to his modern readers that "before the coming of the railroad, a navigable river was an important element in the location and growth of a city."

Thirty years later, not only railroads but highways were making cities, and cities were, as often as not, making rivers. New York brought in the Delaware through its aqueducts, Los Angeles the Colorado, and even the Calumet is being given some economic dignity by Chicago. An urban and, even more extensively, a suburban people were remaking their environment. On the farm, fertilizer first restored the soil, then enriched it beyond its primitive condition. The farm catered to the city and bought from it the expensive equipment for this transformation.

People who live in a world made for them by other people take a view of conservation different in two ways from that of fifty years ago. They make their own demands on nature; conservation is no longer merely saving, or even maximizing in any one direction, what nature has to offer. The modern issue is seldom conservation versus exploitation; it is often prudent exploitation for one purpose against prudent exploitation for another. Of course, during these fifty years, Americans living in an increasingly artificial environment demanded more and more vigorously that some fragments of their continent be kept wild. I myself believe this was not a defense of nature against man, but a creative movement of some of our aesthetically most cultivated and imaginative people. In any event, the chief potential invaders of the wilderness today are neither selfish nor parochial. They are the public multiple-purpose storage reservoir and the defense installation.

Fortunately, people who make their environment have necessarily learned a good deal about respecting others' opportunities and even tastes. Americans grew in civic sense as they grew in cities. Now, the public conscience did not incubate evenly. I am not ready to believe that oil rights to the tidelands were wanted by the Gulf states because the nation needed more oil, nor that the electric utility trade association is as interested in wide and abundant use of power as are certain national and local government agencies. The real issue that emerged in this period was between the doctrinaires of both camps— those who believed all business and all local governments were potential exploiters, and those who believed all "local interests," public and private, were civic minded enough for partnership—as against those who believed civic conscience is where you find it and that it can be encouraged by defining responsibilities.

To operate and improve our artificial environment we made all kinds of new demands on nature, and thus became dependent on it in more intensive, more varied, and more competing ways. This was the second change of the conservation context. After we had occupied the last of our virgin soil, we began to concern ourselves with the soil we were already on. Our perspective as to soil shifted from the horizontal to the vertical. The same thing happened to ground water and then, in 1947, to air itself, in Los Angeles and Donora and since then in other cities. In the short run, this means more decisions as to priority of uses, and more involvement of resource considerations with all other governmental considerations. In the long run, this trend awes us with the promise of energy from the heavy water in the sea, or breeder-reactors stoked with uranium from simple granite. Man, making over his environment, may thus be about to end for practical purposes the distinction between renewable and exhaustible resources, and even the distinction between resources and other elements of nature. Science multiplying natural means also multiplies policy choices that relate to ends.

Meanwhile, a third basic shift in the context stemmed from the filling up of our continental area. The frontier as a continuous edge of settlement had closed before the conservation movement could catch on. But some of the Theodore Roosevelt policies were designed to make good particular deficiencies of nature so the difficult reaches could be occupied like the rest. Reclamation was the key word: bringing land up to par. By the time of Franklin Roosevelt there was no par. Classification, uses accommodated to special potentialities, were substituted, as in the Taylor Grazing Act, the programs for the Plains, the soil conservation districts. Or regions were examined for their own resource emphases and tie-ups. These are the common threads of much of the work of the TVA, the National Resources Planning Board and the New Deal resource agencies. The report *Regional Factors in National Planning and Development* [1] expressed the clearest thinking of the advance.

By the time of the Board of Economic Warfare, we were thinking of our resource problem as encompassing, for some purposes, the friendly part of the world. The same note was sounded strongly a few years after the war in the Paley Report.[2] Perhaps this fourth change of context, too, was an indirect consequence of our filling up of the continent. In any event, the nearest current counterparts to the New Deal programs of putting people to work at harnessing nature to end poverty are to be found in the newly developing countries overseas. In this sense, the TVA is not a lonely experiment. India has copied it directly. In Iran some of the leading ex-administrators of TVA are developing the hydraulic and mineral resources of a river. Apparently there was more to the American conservation tradition than husbanding the resources of our homeland. But have we not a hint here, also, that conservation programs as such, even in the scientific, region-adapted versions of the New Deal, had their role in parts of the world not yet highly urbanized and industrialized, where the potential of nature could give shape to a civic consciousness still in a formative stage, where demands on resources were not yet highly organized and highly competing?

Now, I think, we are back to the questions posed in Mr. Griffith's paper a little better equipped to look for answers.

[1] National Resources Committee (Washington: U.S. Government Printing Office, 1935).

[2] *Resources for Freedom,* report of the President's Materials Policy Commission (Washington: U.S. Government Printing Office, 1952).

What had happened during fifty years was that resources lost their fixed limits both as to place and subject. But the need to consider their interrelatedness increased. An integrated resource program for the nation became a will-o'-the-wisp drawing the National Resources Planning Board off into general economic planning. The TVA did integrate resource conservation not in spite, but because, of the fact that it tackled a modest-sized area, and in that area related all of its resource programs to the original federal plant at Muscle Shoals or to the river and the river's products. Beyond that reached advice, demonstration, and recommendations.

Why have we enjoyed so little presidential leadership of conservation policy even while conservation attitudes have grown and the need for policy decisions multiplied? I believe that it is because conservation no longer expresses a self-contained and self-justifying purpose; resources have become means to ends as diverse as growing proteins, living urbanely around cities, and winning international security. Theodore Roosevelt's conservation crusade stood concerted and largely independent. Franklin Roosevelt's conservation programs were means to recovery and victory, as well as to restoring a natural harmony. From this point of view it may not have been a backward step that when the National Resources Planning Board had been liquidated, its vestigial functions reappeared in two separate contexts, that of the Council of Economic Advisers, and that of the National Security Resources Board and its successor, the Office of Defense Mobilization. More and more we have been conserving for something that seems more nearly ultimate.

It is fitting and proper, then, that we do not find ourselves, after fifty years, gathered in a crusade. We are researchers and teachers of not one but dozens of new sciences and engineering fields illuminating and serving various aspects of useful nature: soil science, hydrology, ecology, economic geology, weather control, water and air sanitation. We are policy-makers in separate but related areas. As Mr. Griffith has suggested, not only are water, land, and minerals separate fields for most of us, but each has become too intricate to master whole. Water supply, irrigation, flood prevention and control: we do well if we can comprehend policy even in those subfields. Twenty years ago there was a proposal for a department of conservation. Now we aim at staffing the President and the Congress better to see the connections among the necessarily separate programs. Conservation crusaders can expect no Armageddon now, but a lot of brushfire wars on pollution, power, flood control, wilderness areas, military versus economic uses of the atomic nucleus.

We have in common our tradition and a large segment of our ideals. The need for seeing all of our discrete professions and programs as they relate to those traditions and ideals is greater than it ever was. But it is all the more important to be clear about what the tradition and the ideals involve.

THE MYTHOLOGY OF CONSERVATION

✒ Samuel P. Hays

On this occasion of the fiftieth anniversary of the Governors' Conference of 1908, we look back into history in order to evaluate the present and to provide direction for the future. Such stocktaking, however useful it may be, invites self-deception. Few can resist the temptation to use history to formulate an ideology which will support their own aspirations, rather than to look squarely at the hard facts of the past. The conservation movement has not escaped this lure. Both its history and its popular battles are replete with a mythology which does not conform to fact. Here I wish to comment briefly on two of these conservation myths that seem to have crept into Mr. Griffith's paper. One is his major point—that the conservation movement has become more mature. The other is his belief that the public interest has become much more widely accepted as a criterion of resource policies and actions.

During these fifty years, Mr. Griffith finds, the conservation move-

S A M U E L P . H A Y S is Assistant Professor of History at the State University of Iowa, where his field is American history since the 1870's. Previously he taught at the University of Illinois. Earlier, he did forestry work for two and a half years in a Civilian Public Service camp in Oregon. He is the author of two books: "Conservation and the Gospel of Efficiency: The Progressive Conservation Movement, 1890–1920," about to be published by the Harvard University Press; and *The Response to Industrialism, 1885–1914,* University of Chicago Press, 1957. He was born at Corydon, Indiana, in 1921, and received his B.A. in psychology from Swarthmore and his Ph.D. in history from Harvard.

40

ment has matured. Conservation today, he maintains, is the product of a long, sometimes painful, yet successful historic struggle, the gradual unfolding of beginnings some fifty years ago. He believes that the basic direction has not changed. In his own words, "1958 is but 1908 illuminated." But the differences between 1908 and 1958, it seems to me, far overshadow the similarities. Since 1908, admittedly, the techniques of conservation have improved, although how much is questionable. But conservation is more than a technique; it is inevitably geared to a scale of values, and since 1908 this scale of conservation values has shifted drastically.

The conservation movement of 1908 was intensely optimistic. Men like WJ McGee, who was perhaps the most vigorous philosopher of the movement, felt that the possibilities of applied science opened up vast vistas of human achievement in the field of natural resources. If one could bring about sustained-yield management of biologic resources, multiple-purpose development of rivers, and less wasteful utilization of minerals, the future held untold possibilities. Conservation came as an integral part of the fundamental changes in human knowledge which appeared in the second half of the ninteenth century —the revolt against formal, deductive reasoning and the increasing faith in empirical data. These changes seemed to presage almost unlimited opportunities not only for the discovery of knowledge about the earth, but equally unlimited opportunities for control of man's environment for his own welfare. Conservation leaders of 1908 were deeply infected with this optimism; they had an abundant faith in technology as the key to human problems; they looked to the future and geared their program to an intensely felt hope for social betterment.

Some of this outlook persisted in the 1930's, and especially in the leadership of Morris L. Cooke in rural electrification and David E. Lilienthal in the Tennessee Valley Authority. But on the whole the atmosphere of the years since World War II has shifted, I believe, from optimism to a guarded pessimism. We think less of possibilities and more of limits; we think less in terms of human betterment, and more in terms of human survival. The unlimited horizons of technology are less often in our minds today than the compulsive use of technology in a race toward world suicide. This new emphasis appeared soon after World War II in two popular books, William Vogt's *Road to Survival* and Fairfield Osborn's *Our Plundered Planet,* both of them infused with Malthusian pessimism, both emphasizing the enormous problem of population growth and the world's limited food supply. Both warned that technology was not enough; resources were not unlimited; the pressure of population itself must be reduced. The increasing emphasis on national security augmented this sense of the limits, rather than of the opportunities of resources, of the need to husband rather than to develop, of the need to stockpile and save.

I think that one of the reasons why the depth of this change is not fully understood is the prevalence of certain popular misconceptions about conservation in the Theodore Roosevelt era. The view is current that the Roosevelt conservationists locked up resources because of a fear that supplies might be exhausted, while their successors developed a more intelligent program of wise resource use. This notion, popularized by those who attacked conservation policies, has got into the history books, but in the light of the evidence it must be revised.

President Theodore Roosevelt, Forester Gifford Pinchot, and Secretary of the Interior James R. Garfield withdrew resources from *many* kinds of land entry, but in almost no cases from *all* forms of entry. Those water-power sites, for example, that were so important in the Ballinger-Pinchot controversy remained open to entry under the Right-of-Way Act of 1901, the act pertinent to water-power matters. Withdrawals of water-power lands ensured entry only under certain laws, and development only as water-power sites. They did not prevent use, but defined a particular use. They were, in effect, a form of land classification. And so it was with almost every withdrawal during the Roosevelt Administration. As a result of its policies, water power and coal development on the public lands did not stop, but went forward rapidly. In fact, it was the Taft Administration, not that of Roosevelt, which withdrew water power sites from *all* forms of entry, and it was Secretary of the Interior Richard A. Ballinger who prohibited mineral entries on oil lands, when Garfield had refused to do so on the grounds that it would stop development. The Roosevelt administrators were imbued with a philosophy of development, not of the need to prevent use. They followed the vision that wise use would provide a resource base for unlimited growth.

The conservation movement, then, has not progressed in one direction since 1908. Instead, it has radically altered its course, shifting from an open, optimistic, hopeful movement, tied to a broad philosophy of human improvement, to a more rigid, pessimistic one, deeply affected by a fear for human survival. Can one call this a change toward maturity? *

As one evidence of the greater maturity of the conservation movement, Mr. Griffith cites a growing acceptance of the concept of the public interest. Past struggles, so the reasoning goes, have centered on the conflict between public and private interest, but with the triumph of the idea of the public interest this controversy has abated and conservation displays a growing unity. Many writings support this analysis of the past, for conservation history has emphasized those major episodes of the fight for public control: the Pinchot-Ballinger controversy, the struggle for the Water Power Act and the Mineral Leasing Act, and the Teapot Dome controversy. But this emphasis is misleading. Public control is not an end in itself; it is only a means to an end. Conservation means much more than simply public action; and we should be more concerned with the history of its objectives rather than of its techniques. In fact, by dwelling on the struggle for public action historians have obscured the much more basic problem of the fate of conservation objectives.

Some apparent victories for the principle of public ownership have actually involved defeats for conservation goals. The Water Power Act of 1920, for example, established the principle of federal administration of hydroelectric power on the public lands and in the navigable streams. Yet that act also marked the failure of the fight for one of the major conservation ideas of 1908—multiple-purpose river development. Ever since 1908, Senator Francis G. Newlands had fought for his measure to establish a multiple-purpose planning and development commission, and in the Rivers and Harbors Act of 1917 he finally obtained authorization of a planning body. But the Water Power Act of 1920, which was the real answer of Congress to the Newlands program, repealed this one meager foothold for the mul-

* NOTE BY MR. GRIFFITH   Granted that we are pessimistic today, I do not think we are pessimistic about conservation—Vogt and Osborn to the contrary, notwithstanding. I think I shall retain my optimism on conservation on the assumption that we shall see another fifty years and that, at least for the United States, science will rout Malthus.

tiple-purpose approach. At the same time that act gave no acknowledgment to what conservationists in 1908 had considered to be the key to their proposal, the use of water-power revenues to finance the multiple-purpose program. The Water Power Act of 1920 contained a single-purpose approach. It did not mention flood control or irrigation; it spoke of navigation only as a use to be protected from potential encroachments from power production. Even on the crucial item of raising revenue from private hydroelectric power production to pay for river development, the issue over which the battle had raged since 1908, the conservationists capitulated almost completely. In brief, it seems clear that in the Water Power Act of 1920 conservationists sacrificed the essence of their ideas for the single advantage of public control.

Emphasis upon the struggle between private and public interest has often transformed real conservation issues into spurious moral battles between the selfish capitalist and the noble public. Historians, for example, have refought the Pinchot-Ballinger controversy in moral terms. Secretary of the Interior Harold L. Ickes reversed the moral judgments in his evaluation, recasting Pinchot rather than Ballinger as the villain. But Ickes succumbed to the same error of permitting an ethical analysis to obscure the conflicts in conservation policy which lay at the root of the trouble. It is misleading to argue that Roosevelt and Taft had the same objectives; they did not. That celebrated controversy arose because men whom Taft appointed sought to modify policies instituted by Roosevelt administrators. These were policy differences, and it is amazing how deeply such questions became obscured, even at the hands of the participants, amid the mythology of morality and the "people versus the interests."

Our own times have witnessed similar simplifications. Preservationists, for example, have cast the struggle to preserve areas from commercial development as a contest between private and public interest. But commercial development is just as much a public value as is preservation for recreation and wilderness areas. As a prominent irrigation leader complained during the fight over the dam in Dinosaur National Monument, "We are conservationists, too." Admittedly, one can choose between these values only with great difficulty, but to simplify the choice by invoking the mythology of the moral battle between public and private interest is to distort the issue. No such juggling of symbols can obliterate the fundamental conflict between preservation and development as perennial and competing public values.

I am not nearly as sanguine as is Mr. Griffith about the "greater conformity to public norms" of which he speaks. This, it seems to me, is a shift in language, rather than a change in the amount of agreement over conservation issues. The new language and technical concepts of "public interest" do not guarantee that conservation goals will be achieved. They do not answer the basic question: Who determines the public interest? The National Rivers and Harbors Congress' definition of public interest may differ from that of the National Reclamation Association, and the choice between them will depend upon how much political power each can wield.

The widespread use of the concept of the public interest often obscures the importance of this political struggle, and substitutes rhetoric for reality. It permits bitter political contests to be waged far beneath the calm surface of agreed-on language and technical jargon, and drives those contests even farther into the dark recesses of legal and statistical mystery, away from the annoying eye of the public. The great danger of the rhetoric of the "public interest" is that it can lull one into complacency by persuading him to accept a mythological instead of a substantive analysis of both historical and contemporary conservation issues.

NOTE BY MR. GRIFFITH   With the views that Dr. Hays has presented—that overstressing of the issue of public versus private tends to obliterate reality—I agree; but I still sense a very considerable convergence. I am with Dr. Hays in trying to pierce beyond the symbols and the myths to the realities. Yet symbols and myths can also serve as norms, and at least in Congress I can witness to a growing search for realities lying back of these symbolic norms.

Professor Hart pointed out the difficulty of a definition of public interest. I will stand on my earlier statement that however much we may quarrel about the public interest and what it is—and that is the essence of the quarrel—I still say that there is a net gain insofar as today it is the *nature* of the public interest that is the battle, and not whether we shall conform to the public interest.

II SCIENCE, TECHNOLOGY, AND NATURAL RESOURCES

The Inexhaustible Resource of Technology
THOMAS B. NOLAN

Technology on the Land
BYRON T. SHAW

Malthus' Main Thesis Still Holds
ROBERT C. COOK

The Barrier of Cost
HARRY A. CURTIS

THE INEXHAUSTIBLE RESOURCE
OF TECHNOLOGY

Thomas B. Nolan

The part played by physical scientists and engineers in the early history of the conservation movement has, I suspect, been forgotten in the fifty years that have elapsed since the Governors' Conference of 1908. And it seems equally true that the influence of these two professions in materially changing the nature of the movement during these fifty years has also been overlooked.

However, I shall mention only briefly the early interest of scientists and engineers in conservation, and shall devote most of this paper to the thesis that there have been major modifications in the nature and objectives of the conservation movement since 1908, and that, to a marked degree, these changes result from the much more reassuring picture of our natural resource situation brought about by the re-

---

THOMAS B. NOLAN is Director of the United States Geological Survey. He received his undergraduate training at Yale University and the Ph.D. in geology from that institution in 1924. Upon completion of the doctorate he joined the Geological Survey. His principal professional activities have concerned the geology of mineral deposits in the Gold Hill, Tonopah, and Eureka mining districts. In 1954 he was awarded the K. C. Li medal for research on tungsten and in 1933 the Spendiaroff Prize of the International Geological Congress. He is a member of the National Academy of Sciences, the American Philosophical Society, and many professional societies and organizations. He was born in Greenfield, Massachusetts, in 1901.

The author wishes to note his indebtedness to H. M. Bannerman, Julian Feiss, and Luna B. Leopold for helpful criticism and suggestions, and to Miss Jane Wallace for very material assistance in the preparation of this paper.

49

search accomplishments of physical and biological scientists and the technological advances of the engineers.

To judge from the records of the Governors' Conference, many of the men who assisted Gifford Pinchot and Theodore Roosevelt in its organization were the younger associates or successors of a small group of scientists, engineers, and administrators who were active in Washington during the last quarter of the nineteenth century, and who had participated in the explorations that led to the opening of the West. Later they had become involved in the problems that arose during its development. Through their association with both the governmental and scientific agencies in Washington and the national professional organizations, they exerted a considerable influence on both the intellectual and political thinking of the country.

Several of the early geologists and engineers of the Geological Survey were members of this group. One of them, John Wesley Powell, the second Director of the Survey, was especially influential.

One of the photographs which adorns the Survey Director's study is of the Survey "lunch mess" of the nineties. This was one of several similar gatherings that appear to have been a feature of the scientific bureaus of Washington in the latter part of the last century. Besides Powell, it includes WJ McGee and F. H. Newell, two men who appear to have played major roles in assisting Pinchot to organize the 1908 meeting. It also includes at least four others who were "general guests" of the White House conference. One can imagine that the discussions at such luncheon gatherings were instrumental in formulating the plans and developing the policies of the newly emerging conservation group. Their proposals must have been especially effective since they were based on the knowledge of individuals who had appraised the resources of newly explored regions and had endeavored to control their development.

In developing my thesis that science and technology have changed the nature and objectives of the conservation movement, I propose first to review the original concept of conservation, next to examine the present situation in several of the resource fields in comparison with that pictured by the speakers at the Governors' Conference in 1908, and finally to suggest some conclusions that seem to me to follow from this review.

I believe the evidence is quite conclusive that the impelling reason for the widespread acceptance of the conservation movement in the early part of the century, as well as the specific justification for the Governors' Conference, was fear—fear of exhaustion of the natural resources upon which the national economy was based, and concern that survival of the nation might be dependent upon ability to achieve restrictions in use that would postpone or alleviate the effects of such exhaustion.

The communication of the Inland Waterways Commission to Theodore Roosevelt, which led to the conference, called attention to an unprecedented consumption of natural resources, and exhaustion of these resources.[1] President Roosevelt clearly accepted this view and in his letters to the Governors calling the conference declared, ". . . there is no other question now before the Nation of equal gravity with the question of the conservation of our natural resources, ...

"It is evident the abundant natural resources on which the welfare of this nation rests are becoming depleted, and in not a few cases, are already exhausted." [2]

This theme was even more vigorously presented in his opening address to the conference. He said, for example, "I have asked you to come together now because the enormous consumption of these resources, and the threat of imminent exhaustion of some of them, due to reckless and wasteful use, once more calls for common effort, common action.

"We want to take action that will prevent the advent of a woodless age, and defer as long as possible the advent of an ironless age." [3]

This keynote of fear for the future because of exhaustion of natural resources was a recurrent one throughout the conference, and was emphasized by some of the more eminent and influential participants. Andrew Carnegie, for example, predicted that our Lake Supe-

---

[1] T. E. Burton, and WJ McGee, Letter (Oct. 3, 1907) to the President of the United States, Theodore Roosevelt, *Proceedings of a Conference of Governors in the White House, Washington, D.C., May 13-15, 1908* (Washington: U.S. Government Printing Office, 1909), p. viii.

[2] Theodore Roosevelt, Letter (Nov. 1907) to the Governors of the United States, *idem*, p. x.

[3] Theodore Roosevelt, "Opening Address by the President," *idem*, p. 6.

rior iron ores would be exhausted before 1940,[4] and J. J. Hill, of railroad fame, expected that our supply of some varieties of timber would be practically exhausted in ten or twelve years. He was, moreover, concerned that the yield per acre for various agricultural products had decreased, and attributed this diminishing return to soil destruction. His statement, "We are approaching the point where all our wheat product will be needed for our own uses, and we shall cease to be an exporter of grain," might well be regarded as wishful thinking today rather than as a matter of deep concern.[5]

Similar predictions were made concerning essentially all of the natural resources. One speaker, in one of the first of the many similar statements that have followed, reported that "The supply of natural oil and gas is limited and uncertain and the amount available is required for special industries." [6] He also anticipated exhaustion of domestic anthracite coal supplies in sixty to seventy years. Other speakers predicted exhaustion of phosphate supplies for fertilizer, one of them expecting it to be so nearly in the future that he reported that "there is not fertilizer enough to be gotten in the market to supply all the American farmers." [7]

Equally bleak forecasts for future water-power supplies were made, and Hill's concern over the future supplies of agricultural and forest products was endorsed. An electrical engineer, for example, reported that "The supply of water power is limited . . . and great care must be exercised to insure [its] preservation . . ." [8]

It is not likely that many of the speakers unreservedly accepted one Governor's prediction that "The American people are on the verge of a timber famine," [9] but the concept of exhaustion was widely accepted and appears to have dominated the conference's deliberations.

Other views were, of course, expressed, and some of them are not at all dissimilar to much of present-day thinking. Two speakers par-

[4] Andrew Carnegie, "The Conservation of Ores and Related Minerals," *idem,* p. 17.

[5] James J. Hill, "The Natural Wealth of the Land and Its Conservation," *idem,* p. 72.

[6] H. St. Clair Putnam, "Conservation of Power Resources," *idem,* p. 293.

[7] James Wilson, "Address by the Secretary of Agriculture," *idem,* p. 97.

[8] H. St. Clair Putnam, *op. cit.,* p. 295.

[9] Edwin S. Stuart, "Conservation of Pennsylvania's Resources," *idem,* p. 327.

ticularly anticipated the current emphasis on wise use. Edmund James emphasized the need for "so organizing and utilizing our natural resources as to produce in the large and in the long run the greatest return in the form of material wealth to the Nation." He also observed that "we shall add far more to our natural resources by developing our ability to increase them than we can ever do by mere processes of saving." [10] Andrew Carnegie also pleaded for more knowledge—"but especially I urge research into and mastery over Nature . . . our greatest need today [is] the need for better and more practical knowledge." [11]

On the whole, though, the emphasis on exhaustion prevailed, and the Declaration of the Conference, adopted shortly before the sessions were adjourned reiterated that theme.[12]

These predictions that supplies of iron ore, fuel, timber, water power, and even grain would become inadequate or be exhausted in a relatively few years after 1908 appear surprising to us today, when we consider the proposals that have been made in recent years to provide subsidies of various kinds to domestic producers of these commodities because of existing oversupplies. The threatened exhaustion not only has not occurred, but for some commodities we are seriously proposing research programs to develop new uses in order that existing capacity for production can be utilized.

I have called attention to these predictions of fifty years ago not to ridicule the individuals who made them, but to make clear the basic assumptions upon which the initial concept of the conservation movement rested, and to bring out the extent of the change from it to the present-day one. We now characterize conservation objectives, insofar as natural resources are concerned, as those promoting wise use of the resource. They imply practices that will provide a sustained yield so far as the renewable resources are concerned, or those that will achieve orderly development without waste, in the case of non-renewable ones.

Increasingly too, conservation has meant the utilization of resources

[10] Edmund J. James, "Address by the President of the University of Illinois," *idem,* pp. 174, 178.

[11] Andrew Carnegie, *op. cit.,* p. 24.

[12] Newton C. Blanchard, and others, "Declaration of the Governors," *idem,* pp. 192-94.

in such a way as to preserve the social and aesthetic values of the natural environment for succeeding generations. Leopold has recently implied that this may ultimately become the objective of the movement, since increasingly the adequacy of supply of such resources as water and minerals has become a matter of economics.[13]

In retrospect this represents a major change in the meaning of conservation—a change from the negative objective of restriction of use (Carnegie [14] phrased it as "economy, that the next generation and the next may be saved from want") to the positive one of better utilization of our resources and our environment in order to make possible better and fuller lives for all the people.

I believe that this change could only have come about as a result of a popular acceptance of the concept that the resource base for the national economy was not in immediate danger of exhaustion. This reassurance came about in part through the development of additional supplies, in part through supplementing existing resources by substitute materials, and in part by better utilization practices. It has been easy for most of us to accept, for even the most casual observer is aware of the increased standard of living with the attendant increase in the amount and variety of resources on which it is based on the one hand, and the troublesome recurrent surpluses of supply of so many commodities, on the other.

To me it is also clear that this expansion of the resource base is the product of science and technology. It is an interesting speculation that the concern over exhaustion of natural resources, apparent at the Governors' Conference, stimulated research by physical and biological scientists and engineers in this field. Whatever the cause, research has been active and has been productive of results.

A brief review of the changes in our resource situation brought about by research in each of the major fields will, I hope, document this belief.

The field of nonrenewable resources—the mineral raw materials and fuels—is one with which I am most familiar and which I will, therefore, discuss first and in somewhat more detail than the others.

[13] Luna B. Leopold, *Water and the Conservation Movement* (U.S. Geological Survey Circular 402), Washington, 1958.
[14] Andrew Carnegie, *op. cit.,* p. 24.

It is especially noteworthy too that even for these natural resources—which as everyone knows cannot be replaced when once consumed—we now think of the means by which needs for these commodities can be met, rather than express concern over their imminent exhaustion.

How has this change in opinion come about? In general, it has been a gradual process that has been in part the result of new or potential production from sources that were unknown or not regarded as capable of exploitation in 1907, and in part through the development and utilization of substances that supplemented or replaced the common materials of the past.

I had the privilege of reviewing these developments at the Mid-Century Conference sponsored by Resources for the Future a little over four years ago; [15] it will be helpful, and instructive, I believe, to examine that review and bring it up to date. It was proposed at that time that three major fields of research had been, and would continue to be, productive in expanding our resource base of the useful expendable materials.

The first of these major fields of research is that directed toward a better understanding of the origin of the kinds of deposits currently being exploited, and related studies on new and improved tools and techniques by which additional like deposits could be found, even though they might not be exposed at the earth's surface.

The petroleum industry is probably the best example of the effectiveness of this approach. It has provided the country with proven reserves of petroleum that are today sevenfold larger than those of only thirty-five years ago. I believe that this can, to a large degree, be attributed to industry-supported studies on the origin of oil and the factors that control its migration and accumulation, as well as a most elaborate and effective development of geologic, geochemical, geophysical techniques and instruments that have improved our ability to locate petroleum accumulations economically and efficiently.

It is true that we still must face the eventual exhaustion of our oil fields and Hubbert [16] has recently prepared an interesting and instruc-

[15] Thomas B. Nolan, "The Way Ahead for Research in Nonrenewable Resources," *The Nation Looks at Its Resources* (Washington: Resources for the Future, Inc., 1954), pp. 314-16.

[16] M. King Hubbert, *Nuclear Energy and the Fossil Fuels* (Shell Development Company Publication 95, 1956), 40 pp.

tive discussion which outlines the future decline in the rate of discovery and production. But his predictions are a far cry from those of twenty or more years ago, which appraised our total future supply as significantly less than the production that has been made since then, let alone the even larger proven reserves that are presently known.

The older reserve estimates have been completely invalidated by the great strides that have been made through the use of geology, geophysics, and engineering in finding and extracting petroleum from the ground. The various types of stratigraphic traps in Texas and the Mid-Continent Region, the reservoirs adjacent to the salt domes of the Gulf Coastal Plain and the Continental Shelf, and those bordering the ancient reefs of Texas, the Williston Basin of North Dakota and western Canada have added to our primary reserves and are the result of the increased capacity of the petroleum geologist to predict, and find, concentrations of oil and gas in environments that were poorly understood not too many years ago. Our known reserves have been further enlarged by the increased yield from known fields due to the work of the petroleum engineer on secondary recovery methods and on induced fracturing in the reservoir rocks.

And we can view the possibility of exhaustion of even these reserves with some equanimity in the light of our research-derived capacity to produce synthetic liquid fuels from the tremendously large reserves of oil shales, tar sands, and, in the still more distant future, low-grade coals.

Progress in increasing our resource base for the metallic and nonmetallic mineral resources has lagged behind that for petroleum, largely because demand for these commodities did not increase as fast as did demand for petroleum products after adoption of the internal combustion engine. But there is considerable evidence that support of research on the origin of these deposits and into the means of exploring for them is increasing both in industry and in government, and is beginning to bear fruit.

We are at the moment unfortunately more concerned with selling and utilizing the products of our copper, our lead-zinc, and our tungsten mines than in finding additional sources to bring into production, but recent years have seen the discovery of new and significant deposits of metalliferous minerals, which greatly expand our capacity for future production. The new lead-zinc deposits of New Brunswick in Canada and in Tennessee, the new copper deposits in Arizona, the iron and lead deposits of southeast Missouri, and the immense rare-earth occurrence of the Mountain Pass district in California are examples of discoveries that, to a large extent, have been the result of research-guided exploration using new techniques, such as airborne geophysical instruments and geochemical prospecting methods. There are sound theoretical grounds for believing that many additional deposits remain to be found by sharpened and improved concepts of origin and by new and more elaborate exploration tools. Engel's recent study [17] of variations in the ratio of the isotopes of oxygen in some minerals associated with ore deposits, and the possibility that such variations may reflect temperature gradients existing at the time of ore deposition offers an exciting example of these techniques. Barton [18] similarly has opened up the possibility of predicting the environment in which ore minerals may be deposited through his work on the equilibrium relations on these minerals.

The additions to our resource base now being made by better knowledge of presently mineable orebodies and improved exploration methods and techniques will be supplemented in the future to an increasing extent by research on subgrade and ultra subgrade material. The study of the distribution of elements in the earth's crust in concentrations that are too small to be presently workable is already pointing the way to accumulations in which two or more elements or substances are present in trace amounts but which, in combination, may represent potential sources of very large magnitude. In addition, increased requirements or new and improved recovery methods may make much material merchantable that is presently below acceptable grade.

It appears that many elements may be distributed through the crust in such a way that there is an inverse relationship between the quantity or tonnage of material containing the particular element and the

[17] A. E. J. Engel and C. Patterson, *Isotopic Composition of Lead in Leadville Limestone, Hydrothermal Dolomite, and Associated Ore* (Geological Society of America Bulletin 68, 1957), p. 1723.
[18] P. B. Barton, Jr., "Some Limitations on the Possible Composition of the Ore-forming Fluid," *Economic Geology*, Vol. 52 (1957), pp. 333-53.

grade or concentration of the element. The impact of more detailed knowledge of this matter on potential supply may well be tremendous.

Two examples will illustrate what may be expected with continuing "trace-element" research, especially if it be combined with economic incentive. The first pertains to our domestic resources of uranium. Initially we were essentially dependent upon the high-grade deposits of the Belgian Congo and Canada; these ores contained 20 pounds or more per ton, and the quantities of ore were not impressively large. Recognition of the need for additional supplies at the close of the war led to one of the most extensive and thorough programs of research on occurrence and of exploration that has been carried out in recent years. Much of the research was concentrated on phases of trace occurrences of uranium and on factors causing local relative concentrations. It has been phenomenally successful—we now have well-established reserves amounting to approximately 70 million tons of material containing about 5 pounds per ton,[19] and are using new recovery methods that have proved to be entirely satisfactory and are installed in a dozen or so new plants. In addition, there are even larger quantities of phosphate rock containing less than one-half pound per ton, from which uranium can be (and already has been) recovered as a by-product. And finally, there are literally billions of tons of easily mined black shales, containing in the neighborhood of one-tenth of a pound per ton, that constitute a future reserve when, and if, it is needed. Lest this last be dismissed as a completely impractical source, I will observe that Hubbert calculated the energy value of the uranium in a ton of this average shale as equivalent to that in nearly 1,000 barrels of petroleum.[20]

A second example of a trace-element resource not yet exploited, but which I am convinced will be some day, is the Phosphoria formation, a rock unit of the Rocky Mountain region. It includes, as separate beds, most of the high-grade phosphate rock in the western United States; and, in addition, it contains significant trace amounts

[19] Jesse Johnson, "Uranium Production in the United States," address delivered to the 4th Annual Conference of the Atomic Industrial Forum, New York, October 28, 1957.

[20] M. King Hubbert, *op. cit.*, pp. 33-35.

of a number of metals, including uranium, vanadium, the rare earths, silver, nickel, zinc, and molybdenum, as well as appreciable quantities of fluorine, distillable hydrocarbons, and sulfur. McKelvey and his co-workers [21] have estimated that the formation is present over a large part of a 135,000 square-mile region. Within this area, the formation contains billions of metric tons of phosphate. In recent years a great deal has been learned about the distribution and amount of the trace elements in the formation; on the basis of present knowledge, a thickness of 50 feet or more of rock, extending over several hundreds of square miles, may contain more than a half dozen commodities with a gross value of something in the order of $5.00 a ton.

Finally, I am convinced that a still further extension of our resource base of mineral raw materials will come about through research into the basic physical and chemical properties of the elements and their compounds, with the objective of developing synthetic or substitute materials. Indeed, it seems entirely probable to me that in the future we may be able to invent, or produce out of abundant materials, new substances that have predictable, specific desired properties. A first step along this line is already well under way, and substances are being developed to provide particular, desirable properties. The relatively new field of powder metallurgy has provided one means of accomplishing this; one of its techniques—that yielding the so-called "cermets" and "cermet coatings"—has been especially fruitful. These substances may be considered as comprising refractory carbides, nitrides, borides, silicides, or oxides with or without a cementing metal. Some of them combine high chemical stability and oxidation resistance with high strength and low density.[22]

Events of the four years that have elapsed since this earlier review of our nonrenewable resources have strengthened the conclusion that was reached then, that "it does not seem too improbable that, through one or another of the methods of improved exploration techniques, exploitation of presently unavailable supplies, or programs of substi-

[21] V. E. McKelvey, R. W. Swanson, and R. P. Sheldon, "The Permian Phosphorite Deposits of Western United States," *Origine des gisements de phosphates de chaux*, XIXth International Geologic Congress, Fasc. XI, p. 56.

[22] A good summary is provided by Technical Assistance Mission No. 141, *Powder Metallurgy* (Paris: Organisation for European Economic Co-operation, 1955).

tution and improved utilization, raw materials for our civilization can be obtained for a long period in the future . . ." [23]

I believe a similar conclusion may be reached in respect to our water resources. Water, unlike minerals and the mineral fuels, is a renewable resource. Thanks to the automatic operation of the hydrologic cycle, our supply is continuously, but not always uniformly, replenished by rainfall. Although three-quarters of the precipitation which falls is returned to the atmosphere by evapotranspiration and only one-quarter is currently available for man's use, we are in this country using only one-fifth of this smaller available amount. And of this one-fifth that we do use, approximately one-half is applied to what are regarded as nonconsumptive uses—that is, this amount is subject, within certain limits, to repeated reuse. Hence in the broadest sense, our water resources are not only renewed by natural processes but, in theory at least, the use of about one-half of them is subject to almost unlimited expansion.

A number of the papers given at the 1908 conference expressed concern over the continued adequacy of our supply of water. Irrigation, water power, and inland waterways appear to have been considered as requiring the preservation of our water resources, and protection of a forest cover seems to have been considered the major factor in such a preservation. Curiously enough, little attention was given to industrial supplies, which now represent about half of the present water use. Nor was there recognition of the nonconsumptive character of the water-power use.

We still have problems of adequate supplies of water, although the use pattern is significantly different from that of fifty years ago. And as the drought in the Southwest of a year ago made dramatically clear, water shortages may have a devastating effect upon the economy of a community or region. Luna Leopold, however, in a recent illuminating discussion of *Water and the Conservation Movement,* makes clear that our current problems of water surpluses or shortages, serious as they may be locally, are basically not problems of conservation so much as they are of economics. Except for the problems that arise through our desire to preserve portions of the original environ-

[23] Thomas B. Nolan, "The Outlook for the Future—Non-renewable Resources," *Economic Geology,* Vol. 50 (1955), p. 7.

ment of the nation, he considers that "all our other water problems are problems of shortage due to geographic and time variations, which, important as they are, can be reduced to problems of economics. Economic problems gradually become solved by the play of forces inherent in the market place. Water will be used in those places and for those purposes which can best afford to bear the cost under prevailing conditions." [24]

Leopold's conclusion is in effect another way of stating that we are now able to solve our water problems, not by curtailment of use or other restrictive measures based on possible exhaustion, but by utilizing our knowledge of the hydrologic cycle gained through extensive research over past years, and our capacity to transport or regulate water on a scale vastly greater than in the past as a result of technologic advances. Our concern is not with running out of water that is needed to accomplish certain desirable or necessary things, but with whether the expenditure of labor and materials is justified by the results to be obtained. Use, rather than restrictions on use, controls our thinking.

I believe it is also true, as was suggested in the discussion of mineral raw materials, that we have by no means exhausted our capacity to increase the amount of water available for use. From the knowledge gained through research into particular segments of the hydrologic cycle, there are good grounds for believing that the usable fraction of the water that reaches the earth as rainfall can be somewhat enlarged over the one-fifth now considered to be the maximum. Current studies on the principles of evaporation, for example, are greatly increasing our knowledge of the relative importance of the factors that affect the process; [25] with this increased knowledge comes the ability to influence one or more of them in a way to decrease current evaporation losses, such as the experimental work now being done on the use of a mono-molecular film of a nonpermeable solid on the sur-

[24] Luna B. Leopold, op. cit., p. 6.

[25] Water-loss Investigations: Lake Hefner Studies, Technical Report (U.S. Geological Survey Prof. Paper 269, 1954), 158 pp. Water-loss Investigations: Lake Hefner Studies, Base Data Report (U.S. Geological Survey Prof. Paper 270, 1954), 300 pp. G. E. Harbeck, Max Kohler, G. E. Koberg, and others, Water-loss Investigations: Lake Mead Studies (U.S. Geological Survey Prof. Paper 298), Washington, 1958.

face of ponds and reservoirs.[26] Similar studies of the transpiration process seem to hold promise. Other research in progress on recharge to underground aquifers and on the nature of the salt water—fresh water interface in coastal areas, as well as continuing study of the mechanics of ground-water flow, give promise of materially increasing our ability to expand wisely the use of existing supplies of underground water.

And perhaps still further in the future will be the possibility of economic justification for conversion of saline water to fresh water. It seems certain that further work will greatly increase the number of areas in which one or another of the several processes now under study may be economically justified. If for example, oil field brines, and other saline ground waters could be economically treated, for domestic and industrial uses, many places in the arid or semi-arid Southwest might have their current water problems greatly alleviated.

I am not especially familiar with the changes that have occurred in the two other major fields that were considered by the Governors' Conference—soils and the foods produced from the soil, and forest resources. But there can be little doubt that the 1908 conferees were seriously concerned about the possibility of an inadequate future supply of food and forest products (exhaustion in the case of renewable resources being an unlikely end-result) and of accelerated erosion of soil, as a result of the exploitation of forest and range that was being so vigorously carried on as our country was being developed.

Perhaps the most graphic means of bringing out the magnitude of the change in our national situation, so far as food and forest products are concerned, is to contrast the statements of J. J. Hill that both for timber and grain the United States would face within the century either exhaustion or become dependent upon imports,[27] with the introductory statement of the recent report of the Commission on Increased Industrial Use of Agricultural Products: "American farmers have succeeded so well in the necessary effort to increase their effi-

[26] G. E. Harbeck, "Can Evaporation Losses be Reduced?" address delivered at First Intersociety Conference on Irrigation and Drainage, San Francisco, April 29, 1957. Irving Langmuir and V. J. Schaefer, "Rates of Evaporation of Water through Compressed Monolayers on Water," *Journal of the Franklin Institute,* Vol. 235 (1943).

[27] James J. Hill, *op. cit.,* pp. 65, 72.

ciency that they now consistently outrun the capacity of the economy to consume what they produce. . . . Though population is growing and living standards are rising, the productive capacity of our agriculture promises for many years to keep increasingly ahead of both." [28]

The report of this commission is really a most impressive testimonial of the effectiveness of the research programs in agriculture and forestry during the last fifty years; it is encouraging to consider that in some respects these are analogous to the threefold research program now being initiated in the minerals field. The widespread acceptance of such practices as crop rotation in agriculture and of the principle of sustained yield in forestry has increased the resource base in the same way that improved exploration techniques have in the mineral resource field. And the success of the studies on plant breeding, on the control of pests and blights, and on improved cultivation practices have had a comparable effect in increasing yields as has the utilization of lower and lower grade material in minerals. Finally, the noteworthy advances in utilization of food and forest products, through the research activities of the Forest Products Laboratory and the Agricultural Experiment Stations, have not only eliminated much of the waste that concerned the conferees of fifty years ago, but have, especially for forest products, actually increased the resource because of a new ability to utilize the waste products for the same purposes as the primary product.

The situation in regard to soils, in contrast to the products of the soil, is basically more like that of mineral resources, since the production of soil from rock is a geologic process and can be accomplished only in units of geologic rather than everyday time. I have the impression that our slower progress in better utilizing and in expanding our soil resources lies partly in our failure to appreciate this, and partly in our lack of knowledge of the nature of the erosion that locally so dramatically destroys or removes some of our best soils.

I suspect also that far too little research has been done on the details of processes in soil-profile development and other aspects of soil morphology. The present practice of soil classification will probably

[28] J. Leroy Welsh and others, *Report to the Congress from the Commission on Increased Industrial Use of Agricultural Products,* 85th Congress, 1st Session, Senate Doc. 45, 1957, p. viii.

be revised as such additional knowledge becomes available, and improved classification schemes better founded on soil morphology might make possible a more rational separation of soils adapted for different use. Under such an improved classification scheme some soils might best be used for agriculture, some for forestry, but others as areas of ground-water recharge or for other water management purposes.

Although the effectiveness of erosion control programs has increased, this improvement has come principally, in my opinion, from empirical trials rather than a greatly increased depth in knowledge of the erosion process. Basic understanding of principles appears to me to offer the main source of further improvement in erosion management techniques.

We cannot of course prevent erosion in the broad sense, any more than we can prevent in the broad sense aging or growth in plants or animals; we can in a small, but to a constantly increasing, degree modify such phenomena and take advantage of our knowledge of the controlling principles in order to achieve effects more nearly in accord with our desires. Soil conservation practices, based on such knowledge, give great promise not only in the maintenance of present soil resources, but also in reducing the sediment load carried by the streams, and deposited in reservoirs. A preliminary report on Brandywine Creek, Delaware, shows evidence of the effectiveness of land management programs for control of sediment; [29] it indicates a reduction of 38 per cent in the sediment load from this small eastern drainage basin within an eight-year period as the result of adoption of a watershed treatment program with practically no dams or other structures.

In general, we can say that watershed treatment programs will be especially effective in control of sediment movement; their effect on the disposition of water probably needs more study before we can arrive at a definite conclusion.

I am also intrigued at the long-range possibilities of research on the nutritional requirement of specific crops, including laboratory studies

[29] H. P. Guy, "The Trend of Suspended-sediment Discharge of the Brandywine Creek at Wilmington, Delaware, 1947–1955," U.S. Geological Survey Open File Report, 1957, 55 pp.

in hydroponics. Further work in this field may make possible a much more effective utilization of fertilizer resources as well as a more intelligent correlation of soil types with particular crops.

I fear that some of my conservationist friends will feel that I have been unduly optimistic in my confidence that scientific research and technologic development have to a large extent eliminated from the conservation movement concern over the adequacy of our resource base. They will, quite correctly, point to a number of commodities and to a number of localities, in which adequacy is far from assured —areas in which ground-water supplies are being drastically, and perhaps permanently, depleted is one example.

But I am unwilling to acknowledge that such existing local or specific, individual shortages invalidate my firm conviction that continuing research, combined with man's ingenuity, can be depended upon to resolve them. To me one of the lessons to be learned from the 1908 conference is the danger of extending into a future that will be predictably in a state of disequilibrium, projections that are based on static conditions. Carnegie's prediction that the Lake Superior iron ores would be exhausted before 1940 contrasts with a recent estimate of high-grade reserves still in the ground that is significantly larger than the amount he reported for 1907, and reserves of potential ore nearly a hundred times as great.[30] And in the other direction, his prediction of coal production for 1937 was eight times too large.

Other examples might be cited, and, in general, it would seem that the more eminent and successful the speaker, the more likely his prediction was in error in the direction of imminent exhaustion. It would appear that this inability to predict accurately might be correlated with the necessary intense concern with and profound knowledge of existing conditions that characterize the successful man of affairs. Conversely though, it implies an inability to comprehend man's capacity to adjust to, and devise means to seek control of, a changing physical, economic, and intellectual environment.

I suppose there will be always a tendency to accept a concept of conservation that is based on exhaustion and that proposes restriction in the use of resources, simply because it is so easy to project the present. But I cannot concur that such a concept can ever prevail,

[30] Andrew Carnegie, *op. cit.,* p. 17.

since it ignores the fact that continual change, rather than a permanent stability, is characteristic not only of the earth, but of its inhabitants. I believe that the prospect of impending shortages or unsuitable supplies will continue to inspire the research and technical advances that will make it possible to resolve such problems well in advance of the doom we often are prone to foresee.

We probably need to fear, not the exhaustion of physical resources, but the dangers of inadequate or belated utilization of our intellectual resources. I hope we are currently rediscovering the need to practice this kind of conservation.

Wider recognition of the part that science and technology have played in the conversion of conservation from a movement based on fear, to one calling for wise use of presently-used resources and the preservation of social and aesthetic values, may well stimulate research by the social scientists and humanists to seek comparable progress towards the newer objectives.

I have not specifically considered in this paper the dilemma that appears to confront modern civilization, and which is at the root of many of the more restrictive statements of conservation: the problem posed by an assumed infinite population in a finite world. Personally, I believe it to be another example of the dangers of projecting current trends into what we can be sure will be the changed world of tomorrow. Edward Teller has recently phrased this belief so felicitously that I shall conclude my paper by quoting him:

> Of all long-range prophecies, the theory of Malthus may well be the most plausible and the most inaccurate. About 150 years ago he predicted that the population of the earth would tend to increase faster than the food supply. Since he made his dire predictions the rate of population increase has continued to reach higher and higher levels—and so has the standard of living throughout most of the world. It is true that conditions are wretched in many countries; but even where life is hard people are objecting not because they look back to a happier past but rather because they demand a better future—which they know can be realized. Human fertility is undoubtedly great, but so far human ingenuity has proved greater. I suspect that ultimately the population of the earth will be limited not by any scarcity but rather by our ability to put up with each other.[31]

[31] Edward Teller, "Atomic Energy in the Year 2000," *The Lamp,* Vol. 39, p. 5.

TECHNOLOGY ON THE LAND

Byron T. Shaw

Dr. Nolan in his excellent paper comes to the conclusion that "research and technologic development have to a large extent eliminated from the conservation movement concern over the adequacy of our resource base." My comments on his paper will be confined to those relating to soil and the products of the soil, including forests. Dr. Nolan has explained that he designedly has touched on soils and forests very lightly.

I shall begin where Dr. Nolan did—the 1908 Governors' Conference called by Theodore Roosevelt. I shall not go into the statements made at that conference for Dr. Nolan has treated the subject adequately; rather I shall examine the facts available to the conferees which formed the basis of their conclusions.

The Department of Agriculture began keeping statistics on crop production and land use about 1865. By 1908 there was a record of some forty years. Crop yields per acre of our principal crops remained unchanged throughout this period. But there had been many

---

BYRON T. SHAW is Administrator of the Agricultural Research Service, United States Department of Agriculture. An agronomist by profession, he was head of soil management and irrigation investigations at Beltsville before moving up to his present post. He has been both a high school and college teacher and formerly was Professor of Agronomy at Ohio State University. He was editor of the book *Soil Physical Conditions and Plant Growth.* He was born at Paradise, Utah, in 1907; took his B.S. at Utah State Agricultural College, and his doctorate at Ohio State.

changes in land use that should have raised yields. Vast areas of highly fertile virgin land had been plowed up and worn-out areas had been discarded. Millions of acres of potentially productive wet land had been drained. Fertilizer and lime use had increased to substantial quantities. New higher yielding crop varieties had been introduced. Controls had been developed for a number of insect pests and crop diseases. Yet with all these improvements yield levels had stayed the same. There was only one possible conclusion. All the improvements that had been made had barely succeeded in offsetting the decline in soil productivity that was taking place.

In 1908 it was necessary to look only as far as 1920 to see that most of our good cropland would be in crop.

My colleagues in the Forest Service, V. L. Harper and James Rettie, have reminded me that at the time of the Governors' Conference in 1908, millions of acres of forest were being burned by fires every year and no effective control was in sight. The Washington-Oregon fires of 1902, the Adirondack fire of 1903, the Chisholm fire of 1908, and the Idaho-Montana fires of 1910 wiped out more than 3 million acres of timber within a period of eight years. Other losses to less spectacular fires added up to a much larger acreage. Forest protection and forest management as we now think of them were practically unknown. Timber harvesting was a mining operation, pure and simple.

In 1908 there was cause for concern about our soils and our forests. And it was well-founded concern that prompted timely effort. Action was taken on a broad front by the federal government, by the states, by farmers, and by forest land owners. Research was given due recognition.

Today, after fifty years, we see the fruits of the effort started in 1908. It took nearly thirty years to get into operation, but then the payoff came.

In 1939, when World War II broke out in Europe, American farmers produced a 2½-billion-bushel crop of corn on 88 million acres. Last year, they produced 32 per cent more on 15 million less acres. The story repeats itself with virtually all major crops. The 740 million bushels of wheat produced in 1939 took 52½ million acres. Last year, on only 43½ million harvested acres, the crop was 200 million bushels greater. When we consider the fact that, compared with 1939, farmers last year reduced cotton acreage by 45 per cent and still produced 95 per cent as much cotton, we have to admit production capacity definitely has gone up.

It is the same story with livestock. In 1956 we had nearly 3 million fewer dairy cows than in 1940, but each cow produced two-thirds of a ton more milk during the year. For every two eggs a hen laid in 1940, her descendant is laying about three today. We have 99 million cattle and horses on the same pastures and rangelands that in 1940 supported 83 million head. We had a pig crop of 90 million in 1956 on the same farm plant that produced 80 million in 1940.

All told, we're producing 40 per cent more farm commodities on virtually the same farm acreage we had in 1939.

Organized fire protection now covers about 95 per cent of all forest land requiring such protection. Utilization of logging residues and of mill residues as raw materials for the production of pulp and other wood-fiber products has reduced the volume of unused wood. Hardwoods are being used in the pulp and paper industry.

But these facts and figures alone don't tell the whole story. Figures on manpower required to do the job also are significant. In World War I, we produced our farm commodities with 13½ million workers; in World War II, with 10½ million workers; today there are only 7½ million farm workers.

This is a good time to point out that I am in agreement with Dr. Nolan's thesis that technology is a resource that can be substituted for other resources.

Now let us look at the future. Carl Heisig, of the Farm Economics Research Division, states that the record farm output in 1957 may need to be increased by 35 to 45 per cent by 1975 if a population of 230 million is assumed. The job ahead becomes somewhat more than double the annual increases attained since World War II. Because of our current surplus situation, the increases in output indicated by 1975 will need to come more in the second decade than in the first.

A study by the Forest Service indicates that demand for timber products can be expected to increase about 30 per cent by 1975 and 80 per cent before the year 2000. These demand projections are based on median expectations of population growth and on the assumption that price of timber in general will rise at about the same rate as price of competing materials.

Compared with past trends in performance the job ahead appears to be substantial. Like Dr. Nolan, I am optimistic about the future. Also like him, I place my chief reliance on science and technology. But many difficult problems of adjustment still lie ahead. The question is not whether we can produce enough, but rather at what cost. I cannot subscribe to Dr. Nolan's assumption that the economic aspects of conservation will solve themselves. It is not enough to say that increased requirements will bring higher prices. These higher prices mean higher costs. Therefore, less total resources will be available to be spent for other production goods, and the higher cost of certain resources will limit the potential rise in our level of living. Illustrating this point in terms of nonrenewable minerals, it is not enough to discover low-grade minerals that can be used as a substitute for the higher grades that are exhausted. It is necessary to discover new technology that will close the gap in the cost of using the lower-grade minerals as compared with the higher grades. Otherwise, more of other resources (labor and other capital) will be required to satisfy the demand.

There are other conservation problems about which we should not be complacent. Destructive agents—principally insects and disease —still take a heavy toll of our forests. About one-fourth of our forest land is poorly stocked. Some 50 million acres, or about one acre out of every ten of commercial forest land in the continental United States, is in need of planting or some other means of artificial regeneration to restore a timber stand within a reasonable time. Much of the timber being grown is of kinds and quality not harvested. Of the timber being harvested, about one-fourth is still not utilized for any purpose —not even for fuel.

Despite all our current efforts in conservation, the soils of the United States are still deteriorating. The problem varies by region. In areas of the Southeast and along the Eastern Seaboard where erosion is being well managed, cultivated soils today are better than they ever were, primarily perhaps because their initial productivity was so low. There is still much serious erosion in the Southeast and practically all southern soils need further improvement. Much of the Northeast is on the upgrade. In the rest of the nation soils are still deteriorating. We know methods to maintain and improve soil productivity with economic use of land in all areas except the Great Plains. In that area the full answer is yet to be found.

We have big problems ahead of us with soils and forests, but I am confident that we can meet them, if as individuals and as a nation we are sufficiently determined to do so. Perhaps we need more of that sense of urgency that characterized the 1908 Governors' Conference.

MALTHUS' MAIN THESIS STILL HOLDS

✍ Robert C. Cook

Dr. Nolan's main theme is the "effect" of science and technology on the "conservation" of natural resources; or rather, perhaps, their effect of making such conservation unnecessary. Tom Nolan and I have never seen eye-to-eye on this subject. In raising some questions regarding the "miracles of technology" and otherwise in attempting to capsule vigorous dissent in limited space, I hope I shall not sound too brusque. We love each other, but sometimes from opposite corners.

The lush benefits of technology have been limited to a very small proportion of the world's population. The 6 per cent who live in the United States have been blessed far beyond any other nation on earth. The success of applied physical science in the western world (excluding Latin America) invites the dangerous illusion that "science," as virtually a deified abstraction, "has all the answers." This can lead us to forget that we humans are part of an ecosystem that includes the biological world, the social-cultural world, as well as the physical world. This confidence in the god Science may lead to a dangerous

---

ROBERT C. COOK, scientist and editor, is Director of the Population Reference Bureau and editor of the *Journal of Heredity* and the *Population Bulletin.* He is also lecturer in biology at the George Washington University and lecturer in medical genetics at the Medical School of that University. He is author of *Human Fertility: The Modern Dilemma,* and is a frequent contributor to technical journals and popular magazines. He was born in Washington, D.C., in 1898, and studied at George Washington University and the University of Maryland.

72

tendency to worship the scientist as a modern medicine man and thus to ignore a great deal of the total ecosystem.

The public seems eager to accept this myth. This is dangerous and I warn against it strongly. Any notion that the laboratory smock has supernatural properties is an illusion.

Dr. Nolan's evocation of Dr. Edward Teller to debunk the current population crisis is a case in point. Dr. Teller is unquestionably a world authority in his specialized field of thermo-nuclear physics. But distinction in one area in no sense qualifies a person as competent in demography or economics. To think that it does is to play the game of the medicine man of science very dangerously.

In terms of limited areas of the earth's surface—and for very special reasons—Malthus guessed wrong, at least in the short term. The people of northern and western Europe and their descendants elsewhere, nourished, as Edmund Burke remarked, "from the full breast of the exuberance of the New World," have multiplied their numbers and their affluence during two profligate centuries of grace. But now the exuberance of a very rich continent has begun to dry up. It is hard to say just how this will affect the way people within the United States will live during the next few decades. Demographers have learned since the 1930's that population growth in this country is definitely modulated by the level of economic activity, which is generally measured for purposes of calculation as gross national product, or GNP. If the present unemployment trend continues and we have four or five million unemployed, the birth rate of the United States will undoubtedly decline quite sharply. I am sure that this is one demographic prediction that will be realized.

We cannot predict what the GNP is going to be next year or the year after. So we cannot predict with too much confidence what will happen to the population growth in the United States. Apparently if we can maintain the fantastic level of prosperity which, until recently, has existed since the war, the birth rate very likely will remain at a high level.

But in underdeveloped countries today where population increases are rapid, the rise is not due to any changes in the birth rate. In underdeveloped countries with a low level of education, the birth rate is pushing close to the physiological maximum. It is not tied to the economic situation. As long as mortality continues to be attacked in the underdeveloped countries by the amazingly effective modern techniques, the rapid increase in population growth will continue.

As long as the death rate is relatively low and the birth rate remains at the physiological maximum, population will continue to grow rapidly. But there is a limit. Death rates can be held down only so long. Actual famine has so far been held off in most parts of the world, but the balance is becoming more precarious. Authorities agree that hunger is becoming more widespread. So with the control of mortality there is desperate need around the world to come somehow to grips with the problem of fertility. I think we fool ourselves when we hope that technology in other areas can give the answer.

For much of the world today there are no untapped bonanzas to turn to. In grim earnest, Malthus' basic thesis still holds in the face of today's relentless acceleration in population growth which is unprecedented in history. Population pressure is now eroding the tenuous subsistence of many, many hundreds of millions of already hungry human beings.

It does no good to dangle before the eyes of these hungry people a trace-element economy of abundance a century hence. For a majority of the earth's people today, it is simply not true that their demand for a better future has any possibility of being realized short of a miracle of loaves and fishes. Human fertility is outrunning human ingenuity today over most of the earth. Here is documentation from competent sources in the field of demography:

United Nations' *Report on the World Social Situation,* published in 1957, concludes that as a result of the various fertility and mortality trends the present rates of growth in some of the economically underdeveloped countries are higher than any that have been known in the history of the human race. Though food production has increased, food consumption per capita in many less developed countries where a large part of the world's population lives still remains below the prewar level. Although food production in the better-fed nations has greatly increased, world trade in foodstuffs shows little sign of improvement. The wide disparities in consumption (including quality of diet) between the better-fed and the more poorly fed nations have not notably diminished.

Dr. Kingsley Davis, Professor of Sociology and Social Institutions at the University of California and this country's representative on the United Nations' Population Commission, has recently written:

> Poor people are more numerous today than ever before, because population is skyrocketing in the poorer countries. If two-thirds of the earth's population was impoverished a century ago and only one-third today, there would still be more poor people now than there were then. With many countries multiplying at a rate near 3 per cent per year, their economies must somehow move ahead at 4 or 5 per cent per year if poverty is to be reduced. This is no easy task when the ratio of people to resources is already excessive and the poverty so great that capital can hardly be accumulated for long-run industrial development.[1]

Many economists question emphatically Dr. Teller's inference that the world's people are better off today than ever before or at least have the hope that abundance is just around the corner. I will cite only two:

At the Industrial Development Conference held in San Francisco in October, this observation was made by Dr. A. Eugene Staley, Senior Economist of the Stanford Research Institute:

> Despite all the vaunted technological and economic progress of modern times, there are probably more poverty-stricken people in the world today than there were fifty years ago or a hundred years ago. This is because economic progress has been slow or nonexistent in most of the under-developed countries during this period, in which their populations have been growing.[2]

A major problem in altering this situation for the better is that with a very low level of living and with population doubling every generation, the difficulties of achieving an economic breakthrough are almost insuperable.

Another speaker at that conference, Dr. David McCord Wright of McGill University, spelled out concisely the economic paradox that stands athwart any easy solution of the world's hunger and misery:

---

[1] Kingsley Davis, "Analysis of the Population Explosion," *New York Times Magazine,* September 22, 1957, pp. 15 ff.

[2] A. Eugene Staley, "The Revolution of Rising Expectations" (speech), *International Industrial Development Conference News,* San Francisco, October 14-18, 1957, p. 3.

. . . The per capita gross national product of the United States in 1955 is figured at $2,343.00; that of Ceylon at $122.00; that of Burma at $52.00. . . . But let us take a more developed Latin American country—say Mexico. Their per capita G.N.P. is $187.00.

In other words, to raise the *per capita* gross national product of Mexico to the American level would require a *thirteenfold* increase in output . . . relative to the *same* population. But . . . Mexico will double its population by 1980. So, to have Mexico reach, and *keep* the present American per capita level by 1980 will require not a thirteenfold, but a *twenty-sixfold* increase in output (gross national product)! In absolute terms it means a rise in Mexican annual gross national product from around $6 billion to $78 billion, to $156 billion! [3]

The almost insurmountable difficulties the overpopulated agrarian countries face in finding the capital to achieve a modern technology have recently been explored in an extensive analysis by the International Bank for Reconstruction and Development, with India as the model. The outlook is somber unless population growth can be checked. The United Nations' report cited above sums it up in these words:

. . . accelerating population growth can aggravate the problem of capital shortage, which is one of the most important obstacles to economic development of nearly all under-developed countries. . . . While in a well-developed dynamic economy the demand for such capital investments may serve as a stimulus to continuing economic growth, the case of the under-developed countries, with their narrow margin of income over subsistence needs, is different. For most of them it is difficult to save and invest enough from their meagre annual income to permit economic development to proceed at a satisfactory pace, even without rapid population growth. [4]

In discussing the Abbé Raynal's dictum that "before social laws existed, man had the right to subsistence," Thomas Malthus made some points on the distinction between rights and powers which the above considerations make very relevant today:

[3] David McCord Wright, "Economic Needs and the Population Explosion," speech at the International Industrial Development Conference, San Francisco, October 14, 1957, pp. 1-2.

[4] United Nations, Bureau of Social Affairs, *Report on the World Social Situation,* New York, 1957, pp. 5, 49.

[Raynal] might with just as much propriety have said that before the institution of social laws every man had a right to live a hundred years. Undoubtedly he had then and has still a good right to live a hundred years, nay a thousand *if he can,* without interfering with the right of others to live; but the affair in both cases is principally an affair of power not of right. Social laws very greatly increase this power, by enabling a much greater number to subsist than could subsist without them, and so far very greatly enlarge *le droit de subsister;* but neither before nor after the institution of social laws could an unlimited number subsist; and before as well as since, he who ceased to have the power ceased to have the right.[5]

In increasing our own power over the fifty years since 1908, we appear to have grievously impaired the rights of the people of many lands. The fantastic increase in the levels of living in the United States has been at the expense not only of our own resources, but of those of the rest of the world as well. The gargantuan scale of this drain on the world's resources was set forth by The Twentieth Century Fund in 1955:

> Of many raw materials the United States consumes as much as all the rest of the world combined. It accounts for about half the world's steel capacity, for example, now that the post Korean expansion has been completed. It consumes more than half of the world's crude petroleum and nine-tenths of the world's natural gas. It is the leading consumer of nearly every industrial raw material, and, with some notable exceptions, is also the leading producer.[6]

This voracious demand will accelerate as population growth accelerates.

In the light of the parlous situation of a majority of the earth's people, the picture is not altogether pleasant. Our standard of living is not now, nor does it appear likely to be soon, based on a balanced exploitation of our own resources.

Marie Antoinette earned a niche in history's hall of fame by proposing to feed the starving people of France on cake since they had no bread. At the present moment in history, we, the incredibly fortunate 6 per cent, having pre-empted much of the earth's industrial

[5] T. R. Malthus, *An Essay on the Principle of Population* (9th ed.; London: Reeves and Turner, 1888), p. 421.

[6] J. Frederic Dewhurst and Associates, *America's Needs and Resources,* The Twentieth Century Fund, New York, 1955, p. 754.

bread as above listed, seem to be able to offer our less fortunate neighbors little more than a pious hope that they will be able to eat granite some fine day a century or so hence. This offer of stone for bread out-Antoinettes Marie with a vengeance. If this is the best we can offer the earth's people in this time of crisis, surely we will have nobody but ourselves to blame when the deluge engulfs us.

THE BARRIER OF COST

⅍ Harry A. Curtis

The main thesis presented in Dr. Nolan's paper is that research and technology in the past fifty years have profoundly affected the situation we face with respect to natural resources and have even changed our concepts as to the conservation of these resources. Dr. Nolan describes only briefly, and sometimes rather vaguely, the actual research and technology involved in bringing about the effects he discusses. It is the impact of research and technology that he talks about.

Dr. Nolan gets under way with a discussion of the Governors' Conference called by President Roosevelt in 1908. He does not ridicule the persons involved in the conference, but he belittles their naive concept of conservation, their unwarranted concern over the possible exhaustion of natural resources, and their lack of faith that science and technology would soon solve all the problems that worried them. I dissent from these views regarding the conference. In the first place the leaders of the conference did not voice the layman's common confusion of conservation with hoarding. In fact, as Dr. Nolan agrees,

---

HARRY A. CURTIS before his recent retirement was a director of the Tennessee Valley Authority where he previously had served as Chief Chemical Engineer. He has been Professor of Chemical Engineering at Yale University and Professor of Chemistry at Northwestern University, and Dean of the College of Engineering of the University of Missouri. In the early 1930's he was Director of Research for the Vacuum Oil Company. He was born in Sedalia, Colorado, in 1884, did his undergraduate work at the University of Colorado, and earned his doctorate at the University of Wisconsin.

Edmund James, one of the conferees, expressed the broad concept of conservation that has always prevailed amongst thoughtful and informed people. Moreover, Gifford Pinchot, who was President Roosevelt's mentor in matters concerning conservation, was no layman. When he returned from studying forest management in Europe he was placed in charge of the Biltmore forest in North Carolina, and promptly demonstrated there that conservation and the proper harvesting of timber are not incompatible practices. Even Andrew Carnegie, who probably knew more about the benefits to be derived from a high tariff on steel than he did about conservation, pleaded for research and practical knowledge, items that would scarcely be needed if hoarding were to be a policy. All in all, it seems to me that the ideas of conservation expressed at the conference were not naive.

The conferees in 1908 were concerned with some real and very important problems. True, they underestimated the progress that science and technology would make in the next fifty years, and their guesses as to when the natural resources cupboard would be bare were in error. Nevertheless, it was high time that responsible people took note of the declining fertility of farm lands, unchecked soil erosion, wasteful practices in the harvesting of timber, the rapid rate of depletion of high-grade ore deposits, and, in general the heedless exploitation of natural resources with little or no regard for the future. There was no reason to be complacent over the situation that prevailed in 1908, and I must say that I see no reason to be complacent over today's situation.

In the background of the 1908 conference, though not played up strongly there, was the question of who is to benefit from natural resources—people everywhere or just a few favored individuals. The Inland Waterways Commission had mentioned "the equal opportunity of all our People" to share in the heritage of natural resources. President Roosevelt was certainly not blind to the fact that for a hundred years it had been federal policy to deliver natural resources to private interests with no regard for the public's stake in these resources. It was even more wicked in 1908 than it is today to impose any restrictions on "the American way of life" as practiced by big business. In 1906 President Roosevelt vetoed a "give-away" bill covering potential water power development. If he had publicly repudiated the Ten

Commandments the uproar in business circles and in the Congress could scarcely have been more violent. The good "American way of life" was being flouted by a willful President.

So I express my belief that the 1908 Governors' Conference not only dealt with real problems but marked a milestone in changing public attitude toward natural resources.

In reading Dr. Nolan's paper I get the impression, perhaps to a greater extent than he intended a reader should, that, in his opinion, all the problems concerning the conservation of natural resources have now been solved or the methods of solution clearly indicated. It seems that we have plenty of petroleum left underground to say nothing of the oil shales. Also we have plenty of high-grade iron ores, more fertile soil than farmers need—to say nothing of hydroponics, plenty of water in or on the land and a lot more in the ocean if we ever need it, plenty of timber, plenty of most everything. I am unable to arrive at such a happy haven of thinking. Maybe it is my own fault that I am still unhappy over many of the situations now prevailing with respect to natural resources. If there are no longer any problems with respect to water supplies, surely this glad news should be passed along to a hundred or so of our American cities. To be sure Dr. Nolan doesn't quite say that there is no noticeable shortage of water here and there in the United States, but he takes comfort in quoting Luna Leopold to the effect that it is only a matter of economics. It surely is just that, and therein lies the trouble, not only with respect to water supply, but with respect to the utilization of all natural resources. Our standards of living are all hedged about by problems of economics, and do not rest on the technical feasibility of using a natural resource but with the economy with which it can be utilized. Perhaps my main dissent stems from my conviction that Dr. Nolan's paper pays too little attention to economics and the role it plays in maintaining standards of living.

Water? Surely there is plenty of water in the seven seas and we only need to purify it, as chemists have known how to do for at least two hundred years. It is, as Leopold says, only a little matter of economics and some day the economy of the purification process may be such that anyone could afford to take a bath occasionally.

Hydroponics? This is another art that has been well known for more than a hundred years and one that still makes newspaper head-lines when someone takes a new flier in that direction. There is nothing wrong with the technology, but something quite askew with the economics.

Petroleum? Seven times as much in proved reserves in the United States as there used to be. Maybe that is why American petroleum companies are investing hundreds of millions of dollars in oil properties in remote corners of the earth. Or is it possible that some economics got into the picture?

In any event, all that these optimistic statements add up to is that whereas the conferees in 1908 thought the cupboard would be bare the day before yesterday, actually there is enough to last until the day after tomorrow. Every long-range fuel supply survey made in recent years, and there have been several, relegates gas and oil to the drop-in-the-bucket category. Now one of the pegs on which our present standard of living hangs is an abundant supply of liquid fuel at a cost in capital invested and manpower hours not far different than prevails at present. Any shift to a higher-cost liquid fuel inevitably affects our standard of living. Fossil fuels such as oil and gas are not, of course, our only sources of energy, and our present civilization depends even more on an abundant and cheap supply of energy than on a cheap and abundant supply of liquid fuel. Amongst the problems not yet solved from the viewpoint of economy are the utilization of sunlight, ocean tides, and other sources even more difficult to tap. The only really promising breakthrough in recent years lies in the possibility of using nuclear energy. Dr. Nolan has mentioned the splendid job of the geologists in applying new techniques in the location of uranium deposits. But we are as yet a long way from having cheap nuclear energy in usable form.

Unfortunately, it is economics which dictates many of the wasteful practices in the utilization of natural resources. The economics here is of two sorts, one of which I call the "little economics" which relates to the day-by-day operations of private companies which must make a profit or quit the game. The other sort, which I call the "big economics," relates to the long-range welfare of all our people. Occasionally government should intervene for the sake of the big economics, and less frequently it does intervene, but for the most part it is the little economics that determines the course of events, and the public be damned. May I illustrate my point here? The companies mining phosphate in Tennessee tear up many thousand acres of good farming land and leave the earth and topsoil piled in big windrows. Rainwater then courses down the gullies and soon cuts them so deep that there is no longer enough earth in the windrows to fill the gullies. The land is thereby ruined for agricultural use. Now the little economics says that it would cost, say, $500 per acre to level up the land immediately after mining, and the leveled land would then be worth, say, $200 per acre. The mining companies naturally say that they cannot afford to level the land. Actually this is not so, for when the TVA started mining phosphate in Tennessee I arranged to have five cents per ton of crude ore mined set aside to restore the land to normal agricultural use. This very small assessment per ton has proved over the years to be ample to restore the land. Here then is a clear case in which the state of Tennessee should have intervened in the interest of the big economy, but did not take action.

The alternative to government intervention, and in most cases the only feasible course of action, is to find ways of making it attractive to profit-seeking companies to exploit a natural resource without waste. May I again illustrate my point? Down in Florida the pebble phosphate mining companies are wasting about one-half of all the phosphate they mine, not only wasting half but so mixing the discarded part with the sand and clay overburden removed that it will probably never be feasible to recover it. It would cost very little to segregate in the mining operation the relatively low-grade phosphate lying in the so-called "leached zone," the part that is now discarded. But the mining companies will not do so as long as they regard the leached zone material as worthless. The TVA succeeded in developing an economically feasible process for treatment of the leached zone material and is now building a million dollar pilot plant in an effort to convince the Florida companies that the material is worth saving.

Speaking of phosphate, Dr. Nolan mentions that the Phosphoria formation of the Rocky Mountain region contains "billions of tons of phosphate." There is indeed a lot of high-grade ore that can be mined economically, but a considerable portion of the total is of such low grade that it cannot be processed economically. Another considerable portion lies thousands of feet under river valleys and mountain ranges and cannot be mined except at prohibitively high cost. Dr. Nolan estimates that in addition to phosphate, there might be extracted about $5.00 worth of other values from every ton of the enormous quantity of rock in the Phosphoria formation. He doesn't venture a guess as to what it might cost to recover those values, but it would certainly be more than they are worth, and one cannot afford to lose much money per ton of rock processed if millions, or billions, or trillions of tons of rock are to be handled. So I think that those values are likely to remain undisturbed for quite a while. It is comforting to know that we have something left in the cupboard, as the old lady said of the rotten apple.

Dr. Nolan has presented an interesting paper. His calm assurance that all is well with our natural resources comes like a cooling breeze from the mountain tops to the fevered brows of those of us who worry over water supplies for American cities, over soil erosion, over the wasteful mining of potash in New Mexico and of phosphate in Florida, over the desert that is moving into eastern Colorado, over the encroachment of sprawling cities and superhighways and military reservations on the agricultural lands of the country, over the waste of water storage potential and power development in the Hells Canyon fiasco, and over the coming exhaustion of high-grade ore deposits, just as our fellow worriers did back in 1908.

EDITOR'S NOTE   Mr. Nolan, in responding to comments made upon his paper, pointed out that he had chosen to restrict himself to the physical impacts of science and technology upon natural resources, and that this did not imply that he felt the social and economic aspects were unimportant. Other papers in the forum series, he said, would deal with these aspects. "I wish to correct what I believe was implied by both Dr. Cook and Dr. Curtis: that my thesis is in effect a negation of conservation. My own belief—which I hold strongly—is that my conclusions place the conservation movement on a much firmer basis than could be provided by the original concepts of conservation. I certainly had no intention of implying that the original attendants at the 1908 conference were either unsound in their conclusions or were poorly advised in their motivation. I have a great deal of admiration for what they did. In calling attention to some of the changes that seem to me to have occurred, it was not in an effort to criticize their efforts as much as to try to point out the much more attractive future that we could look forward to through the use by the social scientist and the humanist of the same techniques that the physical scientist and engineer have used.

"Having reassured ourselves (perhaps more to my satisfaction than to Dr. Curtis') that the physical base of our resources is adequate, we should now turn to research in the social sciences and humanities in order to similarly improve our capacity to live with our environment. To me this is a much more attractive concept than the negative one of impending exhaustion."

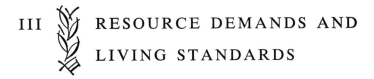

III RESOURCE DEMANDS AND LIVING STANDARDS

HOW MUCH SHOULD
A COUNTRY CONSUME?

John Kenneth Galbraith

Conservationists are unquestionably useful people. And among the many useful services that they have recently rendered has been that of dramatizing the vast appetite which the United States has developed for materials of all kinds. This increase in requirements we now recognize to be exponential. It is the product of a rapidly increasing population and a high and (normally) a rapidly increasing living standard. The one multiplied by the other gives the huge totals with which our minds must contend. The President's Materials Policy Commission [1] emphasized the point by observing that our consumption of raw materials comes to about half that of the non-Communist lands, although we have but 10 per cent of the population, and that

---

JOHN KENNETH GALBRAITH, Professor of Economics at Harvard University, is also a prolific author of books and articles dealing with the nation's economy. Among the former are *American Capitalism, A Theory of Price Control, The Great Crash,* and, published this year, *The Affluent Society.* From 1943 to 1948 he was a member of *Fortune's* Board of Editors, and previously was Deputy Administrator of the Office of Price Administration, Director of the Strategic Bombing Survey, and Chief Economist of the American Farm Bureau Federation. Mr. Galbraith was born in Iona Station, Ontario, in 1908. He received his B.S.A. at the University of Toronto in 1931, his Ph.D. at the University of California in 1934, and was a student at Cambridge in England during 1937–38.

[1] References here are to *Resources for Freedom* (Washington: U.S. Government Printing Office, June 1952). Summary of Volume I, hereinafter cited as PMPC, Summary.

since World War I our consumption of most materials has exceeded that of all mankind through all history before that conflict.

This gargantuan and growing appetite has become the point of departure for all discussions of the resource problem. In face of this vast use what is happening to our domestic reserves of ores, to our energy sources, to the renewable resources? Are we being made excessively dependent on foreign supplies? How can we ensure that they will continue to flow in the necessary volume and with the necessary increases to our shores? How is our security affected?

The high rate of use has catalyzed conservationist activity on many other fronts. Because of it we have been busily assessing reserves of various resources and measuring the rate of depletion against the rate of discovery. We have become concerned with the efficiency of methods of recovery. As a result, for example, of the meteoric increase in natural gas consumption, the prospect for further increase, and the limited supplies at least within the borders of continental United States, we have had an increasing concern over what was flared or otherwise lost. The large requirements and the related exhaustion of domestic reserves support the concern for having ready stocks of materials in the event of national emergency. (Support for this also comes from the not inconsiderable number of people who, in this instance, find prudence a matter of some profit.) Our large fuel requirements have deeply affected our foreign policy even though it remains a canon of modern diplomacy that any preoccupation with oil should be concealed by calling on our still ample reserves of sanctimony.

Finally, and perhaps most important, the high rate of resource use has stirred interest in the technology of resource use and substitution. Scores of products would already have become scarce and expensive had it not been for the appearance of substitute sources of materials or substitute materials. We still think of innovation in terms of the unpredictable and fortuitous genius which was encouraged by the patent office. In fact, input/output relationships for investment in innovation, not in the particular case but in general, are probably about as stable as any other. And investment in such innovation may well substitute, at more or less constant rates, for investment in orthodox discovery and recovery. This means, in less formidable language, that if a country puts enough of its resources into researching new materials or new sources of materials, it may never be short of the old ones. We cannot necessarily rely on the market for this investment—market incentives did not get us synthetic nitrogen, synthetic rubber, or atomic energy—to mention perhaps the three most important new materials substitutes or sources of this century. We shall have to initiate publicly much of the needed innovation, and much of it will have to be carried to the point of commercial feasibility by public funds. We shall have to be watchful to anticipate needed investment in innovation. We will be making another of our comfortable and now nearly classic errors if we assume that it will all be taken care of automatically by the free enterprise system.

But the role of research and innovation is not part of this story. I cite it only because one must do so to keep the resource problem in focus. In the future, as in the past, substitution nurtured by science will be the major hope of the conservationist. I am not unimpressed with the importance of what I have now to say. But I would not wish it thought that I identify all resource salvation therewith.

II

In my opening sentences I spoke agreeably about the conservationist as a citizen. May I now trade on those graceful words and be a trifle rude? Any observer of the species must agree that he is also frequently capable of marked illogicality combined with what may be termed selective myopia. There are many manifestations of this. Nothing, for example, is more impressive than the way the modern conservationist rises in awesome anger—particularly, I think, along the Eastern Seaboard—at a proposal to dam and thus to desecrate some unknown stream in some obscure corner of some remote national park, and at the same time manages to remain unperturbed by the desecration of our highways by the outdoor advertising industry. Were the Governor of New York, in some moment of political aberration to propose a minor modification of the state's "forever wild" proviso as it applies to the state parks, he would be jeopardizing his future. When he seeks to make the highways of his state less hideous, he can hope, at most, for the applause of Robert Moses, the *New York Times,* the most determined garden clubs, and a few eccentrics. One may formulate a law on this: The conservationist is a man who concerns himself with the beauties of nature in roughly inverse proportion to the number of people who can enjoy them.

There is, I sense, a similar selectivity in the conservationist's approach to materials consumption. If we are concerned about our great appetite for materials, it is plausible to seek to increase the supply, to decrease waste, to make better use of the stocks that are available, and to develop substitutes. But what of the appetite itself? Surely this is the ultimate source of the problem. If it continues its geometric course, will it not one day have to be restrained? Yet in the literature of the resource problem this is the forbidden question. Over it hangs a nearly total silence. It is as though, in the discussion of the chance for avoiding automobile accidents, we agree not to make any mention of speed!

I do not wish to overstate my case. A few people have indeed adverted to the possibility of excess resource consumption—and common prudence requires me to allow for discussions which I have not encountered. Samuel H. Ordway in his *Resources and the American Dream* [2] has perhaps gone farthest in inquiring whether, in the interests of resource conservation, some limits might be placed on consumption. He has wondered if our happiness would be greatly impaired by smaller and less expensive automobiles, less advertising, even less elaborate attire. And he argues, without being very specific about it, that the Congress should face the question of use now as against use by later generations.

By contrast, The Twentieth Century Fund in its effort to match materials and other resource requirements to use, takes present levels of consumption and prospective increases as wholly given. It then adds to prospective needs enough to bring families at the lower end of the income distribution up to a defined minimum. While the authors are, on the whole, sanguine about our ability to meet requirements, they foresee difficulties with petroleum, copper, lead, zinc, and the additive

[2] New York: The Ronald Press, 1954.

alloys for steel.[3] I would say on the whole that The Twentieth Century Fund's approach represents a kind of norm in such studies.

The President's Materials Policy Commission took a similar although slightly more ambiguous position which is worth examining in some slight detail. It began by stating its conviction that economic growth was important and, in degree, sacrosanct. "First, we share the belief of the American people in the principle of Growth." [4] (It is instructive to note the commission's use of a capital G. A certain divinity is associated with the word.) *Growth* in this context means an increasing output of consumers' goods and an increase in the plant by which they are supplied. Having started with this renunciation, the commission was scarcely in a position to look critically at consumption in relation to the resource problem, and it did not.

Yet the PMPC could not entirely exclude the problem of consumption from consideration. In the course of its formal recommendations it asked that the armed services in "designing military products, and in drawing up specifications, focus on using abundant rather than scarce materials, and on using less of any material per unit of product where this can be done without significantly affecting quality or performance." And it asked for "greater emphasis on care and maintenance of military equipment and conservation in use and increase[d] scrap recovery of all kinds." [5] But it almost certainly occurred to the able members of the commission that this was straining furiously at the gnat. Why should we be worried about the excess steel in a tank but not in an automobile? What is gained from smaller radar screens if the materials go into larger TV screens? Why should the general be denied his brass and his wife allowed her plumage? There is an obvious inconsistency here.

As a result the PMPC did venture on. Although it did not support the observation with any concrete recommendation, it did comment with some vigor on present tendencies in consumption. "The United States," it observed, "has been lavish in the use of its materials. . . . Vast quantities of materials have been wasted by over-designing and

---

[3] J. Frederic Dewhurst and Associates, *America's Needs and Resources: A New Survey* (New York: The Twentieth Century Fund, 1955).

[4] PMPC, Summary, p. 5.

[5] PMPC, Summary, p. 10.

over-specification. We have frequently designed products with little concern for getting maximum service from their materials and labor. We drive heavier automobiles than is necessary for mere transportation, and we adorn them with chromium. . . . We blow thousands of tons of unrecoverable lead into the atmosphere each year from high octane gasoline because we like a quick pickup. We must become aware that many of our production and consumption habits are extremely expensive of scarce materials and that a trivial change of taste or slight reduction in personal satisfaction can often bring about tremendous savings." [6]

The captious will want to inquire, if the losses in satisfaction here are trivial and the savings are tremendous, why the commission did not seize the opportunity to urge savings. Why did it make no recommendations? But given its position on growth and the meaning of growth, it could in fact go no further. At first glance it does not seem impossible to pick out kinds of consumption which seem especially wasteful—things which reflect not use but wasteful use. Surely the utility of an automobile is not diminished if it is lighter or if its gasoline contains less lead. But this is a distinction that cannot be made. Consumption, it quickly develops, is a seamless web. If we ask about the chromium we must ask about the cars. The questions that are asked about one part can be asked about all parts. The automobiles are too heavy and they use irreplaceable lead? One can ask with equal cogency if we need to make all the automobiles that we now turn out. This question gains point when we reflect that the demand for automobiles depends on that remarkable institution called planned obsolescence, is nurtured by advertising campaigns of incredible strategic complexity, and on occasion requires financial underwriting that would have seemed rather extravagant to Charles Ponzi.

As with automobiles so with everything else. In an opulent society the marginal urgency of all kinds of goods is low. It is easy to bring our doubts and questions to bear on the automobiles. But the case is not different for (say) that part of our food production which contributes not to nutrition but to obesity, that part of our tobacco which contributes not to comfort but to carcinoma, and that part of our clothing which is designed not to cover nakedness but to suggest it. We can-

[6] PMPC, Summary, p. 16.

not single out waste in a product without questioning the product. We cannot single out any one product without calling into question all products. Thus having specifically endorsed ever more luxurious standards of consumption—for this is what is meant by growth—the PMPC obviously could not pursue the notion of wasteful consumption without involving itself in a major contradiction. It made its gesture against the automobiles and then, wisely, it stopped.

III

There are several reasons why our consumption standards have not been called in question in the course of the conservation discussion over the last fifty years. There is also some divergence between those that are given, or which come first to mind, and those that are ultimately operative. Thus, to recur once more to the PMPC, it simply stated its belief that economic stagnation is the alternative to growth, meaning uninhibited increases in consumption. No one, obviously, wants stagnation. But does this argument really hold? Clearly we can have different rates of growth of consumption. In other contexts we are not nearly so committed to the notion of all-out increase in consumption. In 1957 economic output was virtually constant. This leveling off of output—stagnation if I may use the pejorative term—was, more or less, a goal of public policy. The purpose of the tight money policy was to reduce the rate of investment spending and thus of economic expansion in order hopefully to win a measure of price stability. In this context we weren't so appalled by the idea of a lower rate of growth—something approaching what the PMPC would have had to call stagnation. As I write, in the first quarter of 1958, we have had something more than a leveling off; we have experienced a rather sharp reduction in output. But even this, at least in some quarters, has not been regarded with great alarm. We are being told that breathing spells are inevitable in the free enterprise system.

Also, as I shall suggest in a moment, we can have patterns of growth which make heavy drafts on materials and other patterns which are much more lenient in their requirements.

In any case, if our levels of consumption are dangerously high in relation to the resource base, or are becoming so—and the PMPC at least expressed its concern—it would obviously be better to risk stagnation now than to use up our reserves and have not stagnation but absolute contraction later on. Those who sanctify growth but also say that the resource position is serious are, in effect, arguing that we have no alternative to having our fling now even though, more or less literally, there is hell to pay later on. This is an odd posture for the conservationist.

It is also suggested that uninhibited consumption has something to do with individual liberty. If we begin interfering with consumption, we shall be abridging a basic freedom.

I shan't dwell long on this. That we make such points is part of the desolate modern tendency to turn the discussion of all questions, however simple and forthright, into a search for violation of some arcane principle, or to evade and suffocate common sense by verbose, incoherent, and irrelevant moralizing. Freedom is not much concerned with tail fins or even with automobiles. Those who argue that it is identified with the greatest possible range of choice of consumers' goods are only confessing their exceedingly simple-minded and mechanical view of man and his liberties.

In any case, one must ask the same question as concerns growth. If the resource problem is serious, then the price of a wide choice now is a sharply constricted choice later on. Surely even those who adhere to the biggest supermarket theory of liberty would agree that their concept has a time dimension.

Finally it will be said that there is nothing that can be done about consumption. This of course is nonsense. There is a wide range of instruments of social control. Taxation; specific prohibitions on wasteful products, uses, or practices; educational and other hortatory efforts; subsidies to encourage consumption of cheaper and more plentiful substitutes are all available. Most have been used in past periods of urgency.

And here, indeed, is the first reason we do not care to contemplate such measures. The latter forties and the fifties in the United States were marked by what we must now recognize as a massive conservative reaction to the idea of enlarged social guidance and control of economic activity. This was partly, no doubt, based on a desire to have done with the wartime apparatus of control. In part, it was a successful conservative reaction to the social intervention of the New Deal. In part, it was the resurgence of a notably over-simplified view of economic life which seized on this moment to ascribe a magical automatism to the price system (including the rate of interest) which, as we are again gradually learning, it does not have. Euphemisms have played a prominent part in this revolt. Many have found it more agreeable to be in favor of liberty than against social responsibility. But the result has been to rule out of discussion, or at least to discriminate heavily against, measures which by their nature could be accomplished only by according increased responsibilities to the state.

Since consumption could not be discussed without raising the question of an increased role for the state, it was not discussed.

However, tradition also abetted this exclusion of consumption levels from consideration. Economics is a subject in which old questions are lovingly debated but new ones are regarded with misgiving. On the whole it is a mark of stability and sound scholarship to concern oneself with questions that were relevant in the world of Ricardo. In the Ricardian world, to be literal about it, goods were indeed scarce. One might talk, although without courting great popularity, about redistributing wealth and income and thus curbing the luxurious consumption of the classes. But the notion that people as a whole might have more than a minimum—that there might be a restraint on the consumption of the community as a whole—was unthinkable. In modern times this has, of course, become thinkable. Goods are plentiful. Demand for them must be elaborately contrived. Those who create wants rank among our most talented and highly paid citizens. Want creation —advertising—is a ten billion dollar industry. But tradition remains strongly against questioning or even thinking about wants.

Finally, we are committed to a high level of consumption because, whether we need the goods or not, we very much need the employment their production provides. I need not dwell on this. The point is decidedly obvious at this writing in early 1958. We are not missing the cars that Detroit is currently not producing. Nor are we missing the steel that Pittsburgh and Gary are currently not making. The absence of these products is not causing any detectable suffering. But there is much suffering and discomfort as the result of the failure of these industries to employ as many men as in the recent past. We are chained to a high level of production and consumption not by the pressure of want but by the urgencies of economic security.

IV

What should be our policy toward consumption?

First, of course, we should begin to talk about it—and in the context of all its implications. It is silly for grown men to concern themselves mightily with supplying an appetite and close their eyes to the obvious and obtrusive question of whether the appetite is excessive.

If the appetite presents no problems—if resource discovery and the technology of use and substitution promise automatically to remain abreast of consumption and at moderate cost—then we need press matters no further. At least on conservation grounds there is no need to curb our appetite.

But to say this, and assuming that it applies comprehensively to both renewable and nonrenewable resources, is to say that there is no materials problem. It is to say that, except for some activities that by definition are noncritical, the conservationists are not much needed.

But if conservation is an issue, then we have no honest and logical course but to measure the means for restraining use against the means for insuring a continuing sufficiency of supply and taking the appropriate action. There is no justification for ruling consumption levels out of the calculation.

What would be the practical consequences of this calculation—taken honestly and without the frequent contemporary preoccupation not with solution but with plausible escape—I do not pretend to say. As I suggested at the outset, I am impressed by the opportunities for resource substitution and by the contribution of technology in facilitating it. But the problem here is less one of theory than of technical calculation and projection. As such it is beyond the scope both of this paper and my competence. It has been my task to show that at any time that the calculation is unsanguine, restraint on consumption can no longer be excluded as a remedy.

However, let me conclude with one suggestion. There may be occasions, in the future, when in the interest of conservation we will wish to address ourselves to the consumption of particular products. (This, as noted, can only be in the context of a critical view of all consumption.) The modern automobile may be a case in point. I share the view that this is currently afflicted by a kind of competitive elephantiasis. As a result, it is making a large and possibly excessive claim on iron, petroleum, lead, and other materials; but much more seriously it is making excessive inroads on urban and rural driving and standing space and on the public funds that supply this space.

But in the main it would seem to me that any concern for materials use should be general. It should have as its aim the shifting of consumption patterns from those which have a high materials requirement to those which have a much lower requirement. The opportunities are considerable. Education, health services, sanitary services, good parks and playgrounds, orchestras, effective local government, a clean countryside, all have rather small materials requirements. I have elsewhere argued that the present tendency of our economy is to discriminate sharply against such production.[7] A variety of forces, among them the massed pressures of modern merchandising, have forced an inordinate concentration of our consumption on what may loosely be termed consumer hardware. This distortion has been underwritten by economic attitudes which have made but slight accommodation to the transition of our world from one of privation to one of opulence. A rationalization of our present consumption patterns—a rationalization which would more accurately reflect free and unmanaged consumer choice—might also be an important step in materials conservation.

[7] *The Affluent Society* (Boston: Houghton Mifflin, May 1958).

THE CRUCIAL VALUE PROBLEMS

✍ *Philip M. Hauser*

As a demographer and statistician I should, I suppose, be expected to comment on Professor Galbraith's paper by evaluating whatever population projections and possibly consumption functions he might have used to quantify the magnitude of, and the rate—to some the alarming rate—of increase in, consumption in the United States and especially in respect of relatively scarce and nonrenewable materials.

But although Galbraith alludes to the great and increasing rate of consumption, he has seen fit not to quantify anything. He thus has left me in something of a fix: have slide rule with no place to travel. This situation calls for the criticism of a philosopher concerned with the normative rather than of a demographer or statistician. But having been trained also as a sociologist, it is not too difficult a matter to switch to philosophy in treating what Galbraith feels are the really

---

PHILIP M. HAUSER, Professor of Sociology, and Chairman of that department at the University of Chicago, is also Director of the University's Population Research and Training Center. Previously he has served as Deputy and Acting Director of the Bureau of the Census, Assistant to the Secretary of Commerce, and United States representative to the United Nations Population Commission. He is a former vice president of the American Statistical Association and of the American Sociological Society and a former president of the Population Association of America. Mr. Hauser is co-editor of *The Study of Population: An Inventory and Appraisal,* and editor of *Urbanization in Asia and the Far East* and *Population and World Politics.* He was born in Chicago in 1909, and received his Ph.D. from the University of Chicago in 1938.

100

basic problems in consumption and conservation, insofar at least as the philosophical heights can be scaled by an economist.

Before dealing with Galbraith in kind, however, I should like to point to a few fundamental statistics with which he obviously is familiar, that he uses as a point of departure in his discussion. I refer first of all to the fact that the postwar boom in marriages and babies has drastically altered both short-run and long-run population growth in the United States. Using the relatively conservative projections of the United States Bureau of the Census, it is likely that our population may increase over 1950 by some 55 million at the lower limit and by over 75 million at the upper limit, to reach a level of from 207 to 228 million by 1975. Broader limits are possible which could, as Whelpton has shown, result in a possible population of 193 million to 243 million by 1975.

The Census projections indicate in the brief span of twenty-five years an addition to the population of the United States equivalent to all of Western Germany at the lower limit, and all of Indonesia or Pakistan at the upper limit. The Whelpton projection allows for an addition to the size of the nation within a quarter of a century, of a population the equivalent of all of Japan.

Increments of this magnitude, of a population consuming at United States levels of living, obviously point to appreciable acceleration in the rate of utilization of many resources and to depletion or threatened depletion of a number of critical things including oil, copper, lead, zinc, additive alloys for steel, and, on a local basis, water.

The worriments of conservationists, if warranted before World War II, were justifiedly exacerbated by the prodigious consumption of the war, together with the course of demographic events in the postwar world. If one wishes to use what is perhaps the ultimate weapon in the cause of conservation in the United States, it is necessary only to point to the Social Security Administration's (T.N.E. Greville's) projections of future population, which demonstrate that the continuation of present fertility levels along with reasonable mortality gains would, within a century, by the year 2050, produce a population in the United States of about one billion people. If one were to use present consumption functions, let alone taking into account their secular trends, and apply them to a population of one billion persons, I am sure the cost of not conserving our natural resources could easily be made to match hostile ICBM's in potential horror and human misery. On the other hand, it is possible, as Harrison Brown has indicated, that the control of solar and nuclear energy could, with cheap enough power, provide us with an almost limitless supply of "things," from the air, the sea, and the earth.

One can, therefore, depending on one's temperament, be so impressed with rates of resource consumption and the prospect of a population of a billion, as to make these items the significant facts for policy and action. In this position, vigorous conservation policies seem indicated. Contrariwise, if one's faith in science is predominant, especially now that the Army has equipped us with an Explorer to compete with Sputnik, one might conclude that innovation, recovery, and cheap energy will indefinitely, or as far as it is necessary to foresee the future, provide us with all the things we need. In this position, conservation programs may be regarded as palliatives for the more excitable members of our society.

This choice of alternative and conflicting postures in respect of the need for conservation is presented and skillfully exploited by Galbraith. He appropriately points to the uncertainties in respect to the need for conservation. What is more important, he justifiably depicts the vulnerability of those who accept the premise that there is such a need; he then proceeds to explore the problem of what to do about it in a highly segmental and selective, rather than in a holistic manner. In doing so he reduces the problem of conservation to specific problems of values. His discussion is, therefore, concerned largely with policy decisions or value judgments. Hence my labeling of Galbraith's paper as essentially philosophical and normative in character.

Before considering the value questions involved, an observation or two on the question of the need for conservation which may reveal my own bias is appropriate. In my judgment there is adequate justification for conservation measures for both internal and external reasons. In the former category, I would place the desirability of not unduly risking the levels of living of future generations of Americans. Even though it must be admitted that technological advance, innovation, recovery and, above all, the possibility of cheap energy may obviate the need for conservation of many if not all things, it is by far the lesser risk to future generations to proceed on the assumption that needed nonrenewable materials may be exhausted. Especially is this the case when the current sacrifices involved are nominal.

In the category of external reasons I would place the requirements, and for the time being increasing ones, of national security. To the extent that our free enterprise system results in greater exploitation of scarce and strategic resources than does the competitive Communist system, we may be jeopardizing our and the free world's way of life and our national future by risking their exhaustion.

If these and other considerations dictate a policy of conservation then, and only then, are we confronted with the value questions Galbraith raises. His major contribution lies, I believe, in his making explicit and answering in the affirmative the question usually avoided, when the need to conserve is accepted as a premise, namely: Is it desirable to curb the United States appetite to consume? Galbraith is quite aware that the affirmative answer requires increased government interventionism. For he feels, and it is difficult to disagree, that the free private enterprise system will not find a way, via the market mechanism, to place itself on, and hold itself to, a national resources diet.

Thus, accepting the need for conservation provides the first value dilemma and leads Galbraith to the unpopular position that the United States appetite for consumption needs curbing. This conclusion inexorably leads to perhaps an even more unpopular position—namely, that the federal government must do the curbing. The second major value question, then, is that centering on the desirability of further extension of federal government powers that would enable it, like the stern and relentless wife, to force the United States economy on a diet that would be "good" for it—for national security in even the short run, and for levels of living of future generations of Americans in the long run.

As an aspect of arguing the need for increased federal controls, Galbraith treats the restriction of "freedom" counter argument with some impatience. But then this impatience is understandable if one accepts the premises from which he starts—namely, that the general welfare is to be given priority over individual freedom, and that the individual freedom which would be infringed would indeed be far from basic and could, like the restrictions of liberty represented by traffic signals, even increase welfare and perhaps life itself. The choice of values offered here, "freedom" *vs.* "control" offers an endless platform for debate, but not in this context if you are a converted conservationist. Galbraith argues that you cannot be both a conservationist and have the freedom of unrestrained appetite.

In pursuing the matter of social control, Professor Galbraith does not hesitate to deal with another major value question, or more accurately a whole series of value questions, in respect of the instruments of social control of consumption. His references to "taxation," "prohibitions," "education and other hortatory methods," "subsidies" and the like make it apparent that control, if agreed upon, is possible, even if unpalatable. He is probably correct in linking the avoidance of the question of control of appetite to consume with the fear of government interventionism. I believe it desirable to emphasize that his brief reference to the fact that today "the masses of the people might have more than a minimum" is a major reason for the difference between the need for conservation in contemporary life as compared with that in earlier periods, and a basic factor in the need for government intervention.

Not content with forcing these issues, Galbraith proceeds to push the question of control into specific areas, thereby inviting specific as well as general opposition. His observations about automobiles at least show his courage if not audacity; and his references to food, tobacco, and clothing show his insistence on dealing with the big issues first and the little ones later, if necessary.

A fourth major question is made explicit in Galbraith's consideration of "growth," another of the sacred values on the American economic and political scene. This is in a sense the most difficult of all of his questions to face. For we have never as a nation seriously considered the alternatives to growth, even though I suspect there is no one who would not be forced to admit that on a finite globe (or in a finite solar system shall we say now in the post-Sputnik era) there must be some limit to "growth." Galbraith's insistence that there are alternatives to growth other than "stagnation," and consideration of the implications of alternative patterns of growth, must necessarily, I believe, become elements in the armory of any logical, that is, consistent conservationist.

It is now apparent that I have little to say in my critique beyond restating, not necessarily with improvement, Galbraith's presentation. Accepting, as I do, the premise that it is necessary and desirable to conserve our resources, I find that Galbraith has put the proper questions and provided the rational answers. That the questions will be embarrassing to many, and that the answers will be provocative, and considered even dangerous by some, does not make them less apposite. I rather suspect that Galbraith has enjoyed this opportunity to force conservationists to face the implications of their position. In doing so he has performed a service, in my judgment, not only for conservationists but, also, for the nation at large. For with increased maturity we cannot for very much longer play the role of the fun-loving heir who avoids facing the hard reality of the finite limits of the heritage he has dissipated and the need to go to work.

For his part, Galbraith once again has demonstrated his willingness and ability to rise above principles when confronted with conflicting facts. More specifically, Galbraith has, in putting his questions and suggesting the answers, pointed to additional places in our economic and political order where departure from neo-classical economic postures may be indicated. In suggesting additional areas of federal interventionism, Professor Galbraith is, even in this present post-Senator McCarthy climate, indulging in possibly dangerous forms of economic and political heresy. He may, therefore, be endowed with a combination of prescience and courage, or of intellectual myopia and foolhardiness. Which of these designations turns out to be correct will require, of course, the 20-20 vision which will come with hindsight.

ETHICS, AESTHETICS,
AND THE BALANCE OF NATURE

✍ Paul B. Sears

Professor Galbraith's thoughtful, salty, and good-humored paper boldly opens up one of the least popular aspects of the resource problem—namely, the importance of a reasonable frugality. Another basic but unpopular aspect is, of course, our increasing population pressure. This, too, has recently been discussed from the standpoint of economics. Joseph Spengler of Duke University and Earle Rauber of the Federal Reserve Bank of Atlanta have both, independently, given solid arguments against the popular doctrine, "the more the merrier" or "each mouth a new customer."

I feel no particular mission to defend conservationists, so called, against his gentle strictures, yet perhaps I am expected to make some comment on them. It would take a bolder student of life and environment than I am to enter the lists on behalf of all who assume, or have imposed on them, the title of conservationist.

P A U L B. S E A R S has been Chairman of the Yale University Conservation Program since 1950. Previously he was Professor of Botany at the University of Oklahoma, and at Oberlin College. He is a former president of the Ohio Academy of Science, the Ecological Society of America, and the American Association for the Advancement of Science. Among his numerous writings he is perhaps best known for his book *Deserts on the March*. For the last several years he has been studying, through pollen analysis, the climatic history of the site on which Mexico City is built. Mr. Sears was born at Bucyrus, Ohio, in 1891. He received his degree in botany from the University of Chicago in 1922.

The problem of man and resources is an exceedingly complicated one. The whole history of the conservation movement has been an evolution from concern with single resources to realization of their interdependence and of the need for viewing the problem in its entirety. I am inclined to be patient with those who are on the way but have not yet arrived, despite the difficulties they sometimes cause.

There are also several philosophical approaches to the problem. One of them, for instance, is by way of the concepts of accounting that identify assets, liabilities, income, expense, and depreciation. One of the common difficulties in dealing with resources is the failure to allow for depreciation (or depletion) in figuring income. On the other hand, it is well known that the outcome of any accounting system varies with its initial assumptions. Plenty of assumptions are involved in dealing with natural resources.

The estimation of capital resource assets is a thorny job to begin with. Space, which is basic, can of course be measured and we know that the surface area of the earth is finite. Water supply in terms of average rainfall can be computed, but until Thornthwaite's studies of evapotranspiration we were uncertain as to the net amount available for storage and direct use. We know now that for the North Central states this is not more than one-third of the total.

Estimates of oil, minerals, and forest resources involve not only distribution and extent, but quality as well. For each of these resources the standard practice has been one of high-grading, exploiting the richest first. Modern technology makes it possible to utilize directly, or to improve, resources of lower grade, but only by increasing capital expenditures, as Harrison Brown and others have pointed out. In the case of forest resources such improvement has been rendered especially difficult by the destruction of the best seed stock, as in New England. Soil depletion, for example, in Central America, has often gone so far as to expose parent material beyond any present technical means of restoration.

The aesthetic approach also has its merits although, as Dr. Galbraith points out, it is often pressed so hard as to defeat its own purpose. Certainly, sound and satisfying design is integral to good conservation, and it has been true in my experience that Sir Francis

Younghusband, the British explorer, was quite right in his belief that there are only two kinds of landscape that are tolerable—one where man has never been; the other where he has achieved harmony.

While I do not doubt that human aesthetics has profound roots in biological evolution, I am equally certain that it can be modified, even perverted, by cultural experience during the development of the individual. Now that a large majority of people live divorced from primary natural landscapes, any intuitive preference for them is no longer effective, convincing, or even safe unless sustained by some more rational argument. The likes and dislikes of a minority, even a highly vocal one, can scarcely be expected to prevail on their merits, however sound these may be. This is especially true when, as Dr. Galbraith says, this minority seems to insist on retaining beauty in inverse ratio to the number who can enjoy it.

A third approach is the ethical, whose basic importance is revealed in the title of Dr. Galbraith's paper by its inclusion of the word "should." This word implies an imperative choice of ends, and such a choice must be a moral decision. That he has a choice is revealed in his call for a greater measure of self-restraint and discipline in the use of resources. Yet any austerity is tempered by his reminder, following Samuel Ordway, of the rich satisfactions that are possible under a less wildly consumptive economy.

He also refers to "resource salvation" and reminds us quietly that "if the resource problem is serious, then the price of a wide choice now is a much constricted choice later on." This latter proposition has had impressive analytical treatment by Harrison Brown in *The Challenge of Man's Future*,[1] and by Deevey in an important but neglected review that includes a discussion of dietary pressures, published a few years ago in *Ecology*.[2]

There have been some excellent statements of the ethical approach to conservation, notably by Aldo Leopold, Fraser Darling, and Albert Schweitzer. The common element in all is an insistence on ends greater than the immediate satisfaction of the individual. Even the doctrine of laissez faire gets its day in court by claiming

[1] New York: Viking Press, 1954.

[2] E. S. Deevey, Jr., "Recent Textbooks of Human Ecology," *Ecology*, 32 (1951), 345-51.

that in allowing each individual to seek his own welfare, a greater good—i.e., the ultimate welfare of all—will be secured. The men I have named include in their concern a respect for all living things, and for the order of nature in general.

My own rather pragmatic assumption is that the human adventure is worth maintaining for as long and at as high a quality as possible. It happens that this, in my judgment, does no violence to a respect for the order of nature—indeed, requires it. It is clear that Dr. Galbraith is similarly concerned with the continuity of human culture even though he does not say so in so many words. There are times when ethical assumptions gain more by being taken for granted beyond question than by being paraded, and this seems to be one.

Speaking then of practical means, he suggests a doctrine so old and out of fashion that it has all the merit of novelty. He has suggested that we work on the denominator of the supply/demand ratio, by beginning to face realistically the possibility of lessening our present dizzy rate of consumption. If ever I heard a subversive idea, this is it. And if ever I welcomed one, this is the occasion.

Our technological culture, with the notable exception of the medical arts (which themselves are not free from a growing tinge of commercialism) is geared to the speedy elaboration of consumer goods from natural resources. By comparison, the attention given to ensuring an adequate future supply of such resources is meager and more often intuitive than analytical. Yet realistic analysis is essential, not only to reinforce intuition, however sound, but to lay the foundation for effective action.

Such analysis may be cultural, biological, or physical, as I see it. The economic accounting approach mentioned in the beginning of my comments is, I believe, subsumed in the cultural, since I happen to agree with the late George Wehrwein that economics is fundamentally a matter of human behavior. I have long since found it convenient to view the conservation problem as a resultant of the interplay of resources, population, and culture.

As a rough approximation, we can identify a sequence of four phases in our cultural analysis,

Sources → Elaboration → Distribution → Consumption;

each dependent upon that which precedes it. When sources of material or energy are lacking the process stops. If the raw products cannot be converted into usable form, there is nothing to distribute and consume. Should distribution break down, no matter how ample the supply the consumer is in want. I saw precisely this happen in the early 1930's when there were heaps of unmarketed wheat in western Kansas and bread lines a few hundred miles east of them.

At the present time, to a degree never before known in history, the fabrication of goods has been developed out of all proportion to other phases of the sequence. The dynamic no longer comes solely from the consumer and his urgent needs. Instead of this pull from those who want, we now have a push from those who produce and whose chief problem is disposal of what they have produced with such facility.

Man, whatever else he may be, is a biological organism. The sequence I have just mentioned reveals some interesting features in terms of biological analysis. The process in nature from which it derives is as follows:

Materials and Energy (Sources) → Organic Synthesis (Elaboration)
→ Food Chain (Distribution) → Utilization (Consumption)

In nature, however, the process does not end there but is cyclic. It is geared to the reuse of materials following utilization at a fairly stable rate, so that, as Darwin long ago pointed out, species populations remain fairly constant.

What technological man has done is to introduce a vast change into the tempo rather than the character of this cycle. He has, as we have said, vastly speeded it up in the intermediate stages, while at the same time through his dissipation of reserves, enormously slowed it down at the phase of return for reuse. It is this inevitable trend of human activity, rather than any transient inventory of resources or any promise of new sources or technological expedients, that concerns the ecologist so profoundly.

But since physical analysis seems to be at present more convincing than biological, how does it apply to the sequence sketched above? So far as we can tell, during the billion and a half years that life has existed on earth the dynamic system approximated that known as a steady state. Activated by the income of solar energy, a pattern of highly integrated use of that energy, to sustain life and maintain the system in working order, was developed. The interval between energy fixation and its final dissipation to increase the entropy of our solar system was prolonged by the way in which life and environment were organized. Residual effects, such as soil, topography, and productive plant and animal communities, were the expression of this relatively efficient process. The appropriate analogy is an industrial plant which utilizes a suitable fraction of current income to maintain its productive efficiency instead of expending it all in dividends.

Here, in the thermodynamic steady state we observe in nature, we have a model which should be taken very seriously in the shaping of human culture. Speaking purely as a scientist and ignoring so far as I can my own ethical and aesthetic preferences, few things disturb me more than our general neglect of what I regard as the physical basis of our whole enterprise.

Our choice lies between that of an expanding economy (a concept without physical warrant so far as I know) and that of a steady state such as prevailed during all of prehuman biological time. It is most gratifying to note that Professor Galbraith, in his comment on the report of the President's Materials Policy Commission and that of The Twentieth Century Fund, has sensed the gravity of this fundamental decision. He might well have added the report of the President's Water Policy Commission, with its initial assumption of an expanding economy, as well as numerous other more ebullient pronouncements.

And finally, while he has left the thorny population problem to the demographers, it is supremely encouraging to see how squarely he has faced the issue of unnecessary and artificially stimulated consumption.

IV 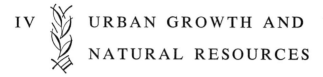 URBAN GROWTH AND NATURAL RESOURCES

THE CITY'S CHALLENGE
IN RESOURCE USE

Luther Gulick

As a result of many complex forces we are now developing on this continent a new pattern of urban settlement. We all know what it looks like and feels like, because we live in it. In fact we are producing it. And we want it and like it, though we also shrink from some of its aspects and suffer with its growing pains.

The statistics and sophisticated analyses of this development have not yet caught up with the realities of the situation. This relieves me of giving a learned and documented treatise describing exactly what is happening. But I do need to give an impressionistic statement of the development as the background of what I have to say.

L U T H E R G U L I C K , President of the Institute of Public Administration, is also Director of the Government in Metropolitan Areas project of the Edgar Stern Family Fund, and Director of the New York Bureau of Municipal Research (in public finance and taxation). From 1931 to 1942 he was Eaton Professor of Municipal Science and Administration at Columbia University. A former president of the Tax Research Foundation, Mr. Gulick has held several special assignments with the United States Government, and has been counsel for legislative committees and tax departments in various states. His writings, which are numerous, include *Administrative Reflections, World War II; American Forest Policy;* and *Modern Management for the City of New York.* The name Gulick, incidentally, was already famous at the turn of the century, when Luther Halsey Gulick, uncle to the present Luther Gulick, pioneered in the movement to develop for city boys and girls summer camps geared to an enriched educational experience in a natural setting. Luther Gulick was born in Osaka, Japan, in 1892; received his Ph.D. at Columbia in 1920, and his LL.D. at Whitman College (Wash.) in 1952.

As anyone can see for himself, urban settlement is no longer closely confined within "city limits." Around each growing urban complex, residential, industrial, and commercial settlement spreads out in a loose pattern of urban sprawl and ribbon development.

These urban concentrations are not distributed evenly every 100 miles across the face of the continent. They tend to cluster in great splotches and streaks. The largest reaches for 600 miles from Massachusetts to Virginia and contains now over 29 million people. Another is developing, running west from Connecticut, New York, and Pennsylvania across the continent to the Mississippi River, the so-called "industrial belt." The Pacific Coast shows another urbanization from San Francisco, with some temporary gaps, to the Mexican border. And other smaller urban clusters are beginning to emerge.

Each of these massed urbanized regions is characterized by the same general pattern of settlement. Population is spread out, as are industries, shopping facilities, even businesses, educational institutions, and entertainment and other common facilities.

And, what is equally important, these regions are filled up with *urbanized people.* They have higher incomes, more education, more sophisticated tastes, spend more, work hard but have more leisure time, change jobs easily, are more footloose, and take to other changes in their stride. These urbanites are more cosmopolitan and tolerant, but just the same they want to live and bring up their families with people of what they consider their "own kind." So new urban and suburban mores are arising, founded on our old values, but designed to fit the new life.

The whole thing is held together by the private automobile, the thruways, mass transportation, the telephone, other common channels of communication, and the unbelievable crisscross of economic and social intercourse.

And there are other bonds of community, including dependence on common resources and governmental structures which I want to discuss later.

The resulting pattern of settlement—industrial, commercial, and residential—is something new under the sun. It is not just more of the old. It is a new system of land use and human organization.

Twenty years from now, demographers will prove this with statistics. But for the present we may take it on faith.

There is reason to believe also that this new pattern of settlement is still in the early stages of its evolution and that we will see not a diminution of this trend but its acceleration. A recent survey in Providence, Rhode Island, for example, showed that 40 per cent of the present city residents hope and think they might move to the suburbs in due course.[1]

The urbanization movement might, it is true, be retarded by increasing rigidities in suburban building costs, more rigorous public controls, or a deep national depression. But even with these, the desires and pressures toward dispersion are so strong, pervasive, and general, that we must assume that the new pattern of vast belts of urbanization is here to stay, and that we will see more and more of our people in these great urban complexes over the next generation.

With urbanization a growing and permanent factor; with more than half of our population already in the metropolitan areas, and more to come; we are brought face to face with the questions: "How does this urbanism affect natural resources?" and "What can we do about it?"

I shall now try to deal with these two questions in order.

I. The Relation of Urbanization to Resources

It is my thesis that urbanization in and of itself, as a pattern of life, increases the dependence of our culture on the natural resources, and that urbanization furthermore makes for a revised scale of conservation priorities.

With the facts now at hand I can illustrate only the first part of this thesis; but I think that we can demonstrate the second, which may, after all, turn out to be the more important of these two concepts.

It is not easy to separate the urbanized demands of men and dis-

[1] Robert W. Pratt, *Attitudes and Practices of Residents of Greater Providence Concerning Downtown Providence* (Providence, R.I.: Greater Providence Chamber of Commerce, 1956).

tinguish them in clean-cut fashion from the general and nonurbanized. However, a number of urban requirements worth noting are clearly visible here and now. Among these are the following:

Water. Urban people, as people, do use more gallons of water per capita for domestic uses than do rural people. However, the difference is not great, and seems to be connected primarily with the standards and mechanics of cleanliness, though air conditioning and other special functions are beginning to be important in some situations. In urban areas, water is used in considerable quantities both for cleansing and for carrying the wastes of the city, as on a conveyor belt, to points of disposal. Moreover, the industrial uses of water have grown dramatically. While some conspicuous expansions are outside the urban areas, the water requirements of industry are heavily concentrated within the metropolitan regions because of the labor ties and market desires of modern industry. Industrialization is, after all, largely an urban phenomenon both as to cause and effect. The threatened water-shortage map of the United States coincides almost perfectly with the pattern of maximum urbanized development except, of course, in certain near-desert regions.[2]

However, the water problem is not so much a problem of greater consumption due to city standards as a problem of concentration and delivery made necessary because the consumers are concentrated the way they are. This is the unique urban aspect of the water problem. Early in the process of urban development the pattern of settlement makes private wells and springs impossible, as well as reliance on local rainfall; it may locate millions of people where the "natural" local resources are totally inadequate. This gives us a pressure on water resources over and above the pressure which would have existed if the same number of people with the same total water requirements had been distributed differently in a nonurban or widely dispersed pattern.

Water supply is thus a dramatic illustration of the "take-off principle" which plays so important a role in urbanization. Just as an airplane becomes suddenly air-borne after attaining a defined air

[2] Edward A. Ackerman and George O. G. Löf, *Technology in American Water Development* (Baltimore: The Johns Hopkins Press, for Resources for the Future, in press).

speed, and cannot in fact remain on the ground, so many urban "problems" do not exist until certain concentrations are reached, but then become imperative and inescapable from that point on. Few urbanization problems arise in a continuous and gradual intensity, emerging by small fractions as each family is added to the community. They tend rather to emerge by major leaps, much as nerve stimulation passes sharply from a range below the threshold of notice into the range of violent response. This take-off situation is clearly evident in dealing with water supply, though the point at which broad community action becomes imperative varies greatly with geographical factors.

While the amount of water which populations will use in urban regions shows considerable elasticity depending on prices charged and governmental controls,[3] it is already evident that the scarcity of water can become a limiting factor both for the location of certain industries (and their employment potentials) and, possibly, also for the further rise of urban populations in some regions. There have been cases in history of great cities which have been abandoned primarily because of the disappearance of water resources. But that time is now passed. Today, when water is short, we don't abandon the site, or restrict in-migration; instead we increase our efforts, and find more water. While this will get more and more difficult in some places, at least until demineralization becomes practicable, the indications are that water shortages will restrain population settlement only indirectly by limiting industrial development and thus employment.

The urban water problem is destined to arise in a new form in some western states, where local water resources have been impounded by great dams and completely budgeted for the indefinite future for "export" and for agricultural uses. These water budgets were drawn before the rise of urban concentrations near the water sources, and will now create an artificial water shortage there. Such budgets will surely be redrawn. In a democracy, no government can long export water and leave behind thirsty voters.

Air and water pollution. Here again we meet a unique urban situ-

[3] New York City Mayor's Committee on Management Survey, *Report of Engineering Panel on Water Supply* (New York, 1951), Chap. II.

ation. It is the concentration of a large number of humans and their activities that creates the pollution problems, once again under the take-off principle. Rivers, lakes and oceans, land and free-flowing air can take, diffuse, and oxidize a mechanically and chemically specified quantity of defined additions without destroying the general balance of nature involved or making the water or air offensive or poisonous to man. You have to go only slightly beyond this point of tolerance to have the whole thing go bad. While there are some notable culprits in remote locations, especially certain mines, mills, and chemical plants, it is the activities within the cities that are now the great offenders. They place a great strain on the natural resources of clean water and pure air.

Not only are water and air polluted, but at times the land itself. In the suburban rings we now have tens of thousands of acres of septic tanks, many of which are already beyond the carrying capacity of the land. Just a little more density, a few more subdivisions, and millions of suburbanites will find that their sewage is in their cellars.[4]

Increasingly, also, the disposal of other wastes from urban concentrations will become more demanding. Already many cities are finding it difficult to dispose of solid wastes within their own boundaries, such as ashes, tins, and other noncombustible rubbish. They fill all the swamps in sight, and reach farther and farther into their neighboring countrysides to find dumps. Radioactive wastes will now intensify this problem. And while the junkman is a wonderful conservationist, we have made precious little real progress in reclaiming our increasing mountains of urban waste.

The cities of antiquity encountered no difficulty in rising above their own rubbish and rubble.[5] But we moderns have invested so much in subsurface works and have such excellent excavating machinery, such firmly set street grades, and have so much putrescent garbage, tin cans, and other junk, that we are driven to burn and cart our wastes away, instead of raising the general level of the urban land from century to century. We too "make land," but usually out-

[4] "How Good is Our Land Development?" *Urban Land,* April 1956.

[5] This is true even of London. See William T. Hill, *Buried London* (London: Phoenix House, 1955).

side the land boundaries of the central cities, and seek continually more distant available space.

Energy consumption is vastly higher on the part of urbanized populations than on the part of nonurbanized people. Present indices show that the use of electricity, oil, coal, and natural gas is substantially higher per capita for the urban centers than for the rural regions. Only gasoline consumption for private transportation is higher per capita in the rural regions, for reasons which are evident. However, the growth of electricity consumption in the past generation has been at a much faster rate in the rural regions, partly because of farm mechanization, and partly because many industrial and suburban loads are now recorded as "rural," though they are in fact within some metropolitan orbit.

While we may anticipate a continued rising standard of rural consumption of energy, I think it is reasonable to assume that urban consumption will tend always to be higher because of higher general urban standards, and because in urban regions more mechanized services like elevators, street lighting, and traffic systems, street sweepers, and ventilating and air-conditioning systems are required, not to mention the industrial, entertainment, and communication uses of power, lighting, heating, and other energy resources. Already the cities "heat all outdoors." Soon they will air-condition it too.

If this analysis is correct, urban concentration will of itself increase the pressure on our energy resources and fuel and will concentrate that demand geographically. It is indeed fortunate that nuclear energy is not too far away.

General living standards. This brief discussion of energy requirements calls attention to the fact that general standards of consumption are higher in the metropolitan regions, and that a considerable fraction of this excess consumption involves the use of basic natural resources.

The median income of metropolitan populations in the United States exceeds that of the nonmetropolitan populations very substantially. Even making full allowance for educational differences, individual incomes in the biggest urban centers average per head $500 to $1,000 a year respectively over the averages for the rural nonfarm and the rural farm income levels. This is a very substantial differential and rises directly with urbanization. The larger the city complex, the higher the average income.[6]

Since savings ratios are actually higher in the rural regions for comparable income levels, rising with each level,[7] it would appear that metropolitan populations spend many more consumer dollars than the comparable nonmetropolitan populations. This is borne out by such cost-of-living computations, market analyses, and other consumer statistics as we have.[8]

How many of these added dollars earned and spent go into the consumption of national resources? We do not know on a comprehensive basis, and the ratios vary from one commodity or service to another. But where the personal income and expenditure is 50 per cent or 90 per cent higher, the drain on resources cannot be far behind, even though part of the higher costs go—especially for the upper income groups—into quality workmanship and services rather than into added raw materials, food and energy resources. With every possible allowance, however, for these divergencies, the fact remains that people who live in an urbanized pattern make a greater drain on resources than the same number of people living in a rural pattern. This is, no doubt, one of the reasons for the current nation-wide climb in per capita consumption. It is, in part, directly related to urbanization.

In making these comparisons we need also to remember that there are some economies of scale which emerge when men live in congested regions. There is, for example, far less paved highway per family in New York City than there is in Greensboro, Vermont, and the amount of electric wiring and of lead, iron, copper, and ceramic piping and conduits in a rural or suburban area per capita will

[6] Otis D. Duncan and Albert J. Reiss, Jr., *Social Characteristics of Urban and Rural Communities, 1950* (New York: John Wiley & Sons, 1956), Chap. 9; Herman P. Miller, *Income of the American People* (New York: John Wiley & Sons, 1955), Chap. 4; Nathan Koffsky, "Farm and Urban Purchasing Power" in National Bureau of Economic Research, *Studies in Income and Wealth*, Vol. XI, 1949.

[7] Dorothy S. Brady and Rose D. Friedman, "Savings and the Income Distribution," in National Bureau of Economic Research, *Studies in Income and Wealth*, Vol. X, 1947.

[8] D. J. Bogue, *The Structure of the Metropolitan Community* (Ann Arbor: University of Michigan, 1949).

greatly exceed that in a solidly built-up city. The suburban drain on certain of these resources, per capita, is terrific.[9]

Building materials also show a markedly different use pattern. In the rural areas wood predominates as a building material; in the urban areas, more and more, the materials used are iron, steel, cement, copper, aluminum, tin, glass, bricks, ceramics, stone, and plastics. In other words, urban populations, though they have fewer and smaller rooms per family, use more nonrenewable construction resources than do the nonurbanites, with their much greater use of wood.[10]

This is accentuated by the increasing demand for fireproof construction in the cities, and by the location there of a preponderant share of the massive governmental, terminal, educational, administrative, cultural, entertainment, religious and other typically "city" edifices.

While no one has endeavored to translate these factors into natural resource terms, we must not overlook the fact that, during these years of rapid urbanization, this dramatic movement to the cities and the suburbs will of itself considerably step up the drain on those resources which go to build and to service city populations as contrasted with rural populations.

Here I want to develop further the point I noted earlier, that we cannot prove fully, or balance out satisfactorily and finally, the scale factors involved in urbanization. As it stands now, urban populations have, as I have indicated, more education, higher incomes, lower comparable savings, and greater personal consumption of manufactured commodities. The income figures used are adjusted for educational differences, the savings figures for income levels, and the effort has been made in cost-of-living figures to adjust for family patterns. But, we may well ask, what happens if and when the differences in education, families, and incomes disappear, as is the objective of many social measures? Might we not then find that the economies of scale equal or exceed the costs of scale, so that dense

[9] Walter Isard and Robert E. Coughlin, *Municipal Costs and Revenues Resulting from Community Growth* (Wellesley, Mass.: Chandler-Davis, 1957).

[10] J. Frederic Dewhurst and Associates, *America's Needs and Resources* (New York: Twentieth Century Fund, 1947), Chap. 8.

urban settlement would then turn out to show a lesser drain on resources than a predominantly rural pattern of settlement?

As to this speculation, may I say that when this happens everybody will have been urbanized. All standards will have been revised upward to city levels. Furthermore, are there not reasons for believing that this is in fact improbable, in that the income and standards of metropolitan man will be continually pushing forward, while the nonurban man is catching up? In the metropolis, under a free economy with its greater market choices, will not incomes, education, and fluidity always be higher, with deep economic and social significance? Finally, what I am talking about is the next two generations, not the indefinite future. During this more limited period urbanization certainly throws added pressures on our natural resources, because urbanization and the effective demand for higher standards now seem to run together.

Recreational opportunities. Urbanization, as has been indicated, is not solely a matter of a place to live. It is a way of life. In discussing recreation, three elements of this rapidly spreading way of life deserve special attention.

In the first place, as already noted, urban populations have more leisure time, laid out on a fixed timetable, known in advance, and available for chosen activities. The short work day and week, the "long week-end," and vacations with pay, are an urban development.

In the second place, urban populations alone have the self-evident need and desire to "get out of the crowds into the country," and to own second homes or shacks "away from it all," or to have sailboats and motor cruisers.

Finally, there is in the cities a growing cultural sanction for travel, trips, vacations, and country or beach clubs, stimulated by example, advertising, and all the other social and economic forces. People who don't "go away" for their holidays almost have to apologize. The urban "Joneses" we are keeping up with are always picnicking, skiing, boating, or enjoying the sunshine or cool breezes somewhere far away! And what is particularly important now is that these are rich and memorable family activities, in contrast with so much of urban life.

Because of these factors, and the now universal private automobile ownership potential—based in considerable measure on high general incomes and our extraordinary secondhand car market—urban populations are now the great "consumers" of national parks, seaside resorts, lakes and coastal waters, state parks and parkways, and the "open country." The exodus by car from the cities to the shore and mountains on every possible day, and during the vacation and holiday seasons, is already a terrific factor in our national life.[11] And no one knows how soon we will also take to the air in significant numbers to reach for fun. The rural sportsman should also be mentioned; the increased demand from nonmetropolitan folks also for recreational resources, especially for fishing, hunting, swimming and motoring, cannot be overlooked in this connection. But it is the urban man added to the natural local recreational activity, that overfishes, overhunts, and overcrowds the facilities.

I have never seen figures that measure a decent provision of seaside, mountain, lake, wilderness, country and open vistas as a recreation resource and spiritual delight for urban denizens. But I do know that we are already, at times, turning our great parks, like Yellowstone and Yosemite, into crowded wilderness slums, and that you can hardly hear the white-throated sparrow on the trails of the White Mountains because of the babble of city voices!

What will the situation be in 50 years, in 100 years, in 200 years, the way things are going now?

This is clear: the growing urban regions, with their expanding economic activities, their millions of added homes and cars, and their increasing leisure time, will need and demand more acres of open space within easy reach, more resources for wide, uncrowded, free re-creation of bodies, minds, and spirits.

There is a special reason for thus stressing action now to reserve open spaces for future use. That reason is democracy. Why do I say this? Because dictatorships and strong class or bureaucratic governments can correct their errors as to the reservation of open spaces later on. But in such a society as ours, built on private ownerships

[11] Marion Clawson, *Statistics on Outdoor Recreation* (Washington: Resources for the Future, 1958).

and democracy, once land is occupied and developed and is operating satisfactorily, economically and socially, it becomes virtually impossible, even on payment of heavy damages to disturb the status quo, because of the sheer weight of political force. The only politically safe, economically wise, and humanely just way to proceed, therefore, is to reserve the land in advance.[12] If in the process, we take more than we need, this is an error that can be easily corrected. If we take too little, we may be tied to our blunder forever.

And we shall need totally new concepts of recreation, guided by our new psychological knowledge, matched to urban life and the changing age pattern of our people. We need active programs for some, contemplative opportunities for many, and glimpses of beauty for all—even in the confines of the urban design itself.

Thus here again, as to recreation, we have requirements which become suddenly significant not so much because of the total size of our national population as because of the urbanized pattern of settlement and civilization and the concentration of these densities in specific geographic regions.   ·

Land. Directly related to these observations on recreational resources, is the question of land and of the impact of urban development on our national land resource.

Each decade we are now extending our urban settlement over an added 15,000 square miles of land in and around our metropolitan complexes.[13] In the next decade, at current rates, the *added* urbanized acreage will be as large as the total land area of Rhode Island, Connecticut, New Jersey, and Delaware put together. In addition, major new factories, initially outside these urban settlements, frequently take hundreds of acres at a clip.

There is a very considerable acreage required for our new thruways, with their desirable protective margins, and for airports and

[12] Reservation can be made by purchase, acquisition of development rights, solicitation of bequests, and in some rare cases by zoning. The most effective is outright purchase. See "The Cities' Threat to Open Land," *Architectural Forum,* January 1958.

[13] Wilfred Owen, "What Do We Want the Highway System To Do?," in *Financing Highways* (Princeton: Tax Institute, 1957); Robinson Newcomb, "What Can We Get Under the New Highway System?," *ibid.*

military establishments.[14] While these are not all purely urban-generated facilities, it would hardly be contended that the thruways are farm-to-market necessities, or that the airports are not directly related to the cities.

Another major urban land use is found in the development of watersheds for expanding city water systems. Fortunately, with proper management, the watershed may also become a recreational resource, so that these two uses may be accommodated, as may timber and recreation in our national and state forests, and water control, power and recreation in our flood control projects.

As a result of the pushing out of urban sprawl, we are now face to face with other important problems of rational land use. Notably in California, Florida, Pennsylvania, and New Jersey, city "developments" are destroying some of the finest and most productive agricultural land on the continent. Certain of these soil, climate, and cultural combinations are unmatched and all but irreplaceable, and have been the source of important percentages of the crops for which they have long been famous. Their orchards, vineyards, and truck gardens are among the most productive and satisfying in the world, a wonderful spiritual resource, also, for nearby urban human tensions. Yet the city sprawl engulfs them, as "progress" marches on and the bulldozer and the "developer" push their degrading operations.[15]

As I have observed elsewhere, this encroachment of urbanization into the richest agricultural lands is not solely a Western phenomenon. It exists also in Asia, even at the cost of reducing standards of living still further and contributing to the recurrent waves of starvation, as in India and China.[16]

Measured in immediate dollars, I will admit that the recorded owner of the "fee simple" to a Santa Clara County farm will derive more for his orchard as California building lots than for raising

[14] The President's Materials Policy Commission (Paley Commission) estimated in 1952 that 15 million acres of farm land would be taken by the growth of cities, roads and airports from 1950 to 1975. *Resources for Freedom* (Washington: U.S. Government Printing Office, 1952), Vol. I, p. 48.

[15] William H. Whyte, Jr., "Urban Sprawl," *Fortune,* January 1958.

[16] Luther Gulick, "Metropolitan Expansion and Public Administration," paper delivered at Association for the Advancement of Science, December 1957, p. 4.

prunes. This looks like "shifting to the higher use" measured by our private economic yardstick, which is generally pretty dependable. The action of the "owner" is certainly rational for him, especially when you look at his land taxes.

The real damage in the United States is probably not agricultural or economic. The loss in the change-over from orchards, vineyards, truck gardens, and dairy farms to building lots falls not upon the old or the new owners; it falls on the public. It is the urban folks who lose the sight and knowledge of self-sustaining green belts. Where we wish to preserve these, we shall need prompt action, as William Whyte has recently suggested.[17]

Of course concentration of population in urban centers and in great metropolitan complexes takes less total acreage than if the same population were spread out over rural farm, nonfarm, and small village settlements, though we must make some allowance for the fact that many rural, as well as suburban, homes are on land that would not be farmed in any case. In logic, however, urbanization should not produce an increased land shortage, but just the opposite. Ultimately urbanization will make possible the true conservation of land. However, this possibility is not now being realized, and the urban expansions now are sprawled out at the expense of much economically useful and beautiful acreage, while much of the vacated acreage is found unused right in the city centers and in far-scattered and submarginal rural regions, and a great deal of land between the ribbons and the sprawls is spoiled for decades. Thus urbanization does increase the pressure on land as a resource, and accentuates the need for planned controls and for vigorous programs of land conservation and use.

Flood control. Flood and erosion control are generally discussed as a water and land problem in terms of preserving the soil, protecting vast farming areas, conserving water, facilitating navigation, and saving human and animal life.[18] Flood and erosion control are also an urban necessity. It is when men are settled in dense urban pat-

[17] Whyte, *op. cit.*

[18] Gilbert F. White, *Human Adjustment to Floods*, Department of Geography, Paper 29 (Chicago: University of Chicago, 1945); Commission on Organization of the Executive Branch of the Government (Hoover Commission), *Water Resources and Power* (Washington: U.S. Government Printing Office, 1955).

terns that the real dangers of floods both to life and to the transportational and economic structure rise to the point of demanding action. There were floods on the Ohio, the Tennessee, the Connecticut and the Allegheny for thousands of years before Europeans reached their banks and built cities in their flood plains. Even on the Mississippi, was it not primarily the building of cities which turned the natural flooding into a "problem"? While this is less true of erosion, perhaps, we must not forget that the silting of water reservoirs is already becoming a matter of concern to the cities, and that urban costs of living will be directly affected by any major impoverishment of our agricultural land resources. This, however, I class as a general national problem rather than one which is created by urbanization. The erosion of beaches, however, is a direct city problem. It is primarily the urbanites who make the shore so valuable.

The combined resource impacts. Looking at these various impacts together, I think it can be demonstrated that the pattern of human settlement known as "urbanization" brings on a higher and different drain on national resources than is involved in a nonurban pattern of life. Those who make resource projections and draw conservation programs need to have this in mind.

The new pressures which are shown in all the projections arise not alone from population growth, not alone from higher consumption standards, but also from the new pattern of settlement and life, that is, from urbanism.

This is certainly clear as to water resources, air and water pollution, mass rubbish dumps, energy consumption, flood control, resources required to meet the higher standards of urban folk, the provision of open spaces for recreation and relaxation, and particularly land use.

While there is on this continent plenty of suitable land to meet all our urban requirements for the foreseeable future, and to meet our agricultural needs also, the formless and unrestrained explosion of the urban regions into the countryside now going on, and the growing needs of urban populations for other land resources, as for watersheds, transportation avenues and air terminals, and for recreation, greenbelts and open spaces, make us now take a new hard look at land as a resource in relation to urbanization.

The transition of our continent to a predominantly urbanized pattern of settlement, with great new intermeshed metropolitan concentrations, thus calls for new approaches and new public policies.

II. New Lines of Conservation

This statement of the problem of conservation of national resources throws the emphasis on the added pressures created by our rapidly spreading urbanized settlement and the changing pattern of demand, and brings me to our second question, "What can be done about it?"

I shall not deal with the reduction of population growth as a solution, since population policy is a wider matter, not a problem of urbanism. However, I might at least suggest that rates of population growth are in fact extraordinarily flexible as shown by the recent past histories of France, Ireland, and the United States, and the fertility pattern of several "undisturbed" cultures, and are dictated more by cultural standards and public policy than most alarmists have appreciated. Given a rising education, greatly stimulated by urbanism, along with generally rising standards and advancing medical knowledge, is it not possible that population pressures may be brought into far better ecological balance than most projections now postulate? The sudden export from the Western World of public health techniques and of our economic and political gospels has certainly dramatically upset human equilibria in Asia and elsewhere. We have a great deal to answer for, and have been unbelievably naïve in thinking that our cultural standards, developed against the background of our plentiful resources, have validity for populations with no such resource abundance.[19] But we do not underrate the probability that the resulting increasing pressures around the world and, ultimately, even here, will induce social, political, and fundamental cultural changes which will bring men and resources into better balance than is now so freely predicted from the mere projection of existing trends?

[19] Bertrand de Jouvenel, "From Political Economy to Political Ecology," *Bulletin of the Atomic Scientists* (Chicago), October 1957, p. 287.

However, the main reason for not considering the reduction of population growth as a "solution" of the problem I am discussing is that the evidence indicates that urbanism will go right on developing in the United States, regardless of population growth. The new pattern of agglomeration comes not primarily from population pressure but from other forces which have been set forth recently and do not need to be reviewed here.[20]

Accordingly I start with the acceptance of the proposition that urbanization will go forward on this continent, along the lines indicated, for the foreseeable future, and that the increasing resource pressures we have identified will become more and not less severe as we shift more and more into the urban pattern of social and economic settlement.

I repeat, "What can we do about this situation?"

Three things, it seems to me. The *first* is to develop better knowledge as to the new patterns of urban need. The *second* is to develop in urban man a new awareness of his relation to the world of nature and to convince him of the moral necessity of sustaining human life more and more from the renewable resources, rather than from the limited and exhaustible accumulations. *Third* is to take public and private action to develop and enforce such a system of life.

My assumptions as to the unique urban impacts on resources need to be explored. In some cases, we need new statistical and census categories as the basis for understanding.[21] In other cases, the facts are there, but they have never been analyzed from the point of view here suggested.

The whole business of the costs and the economies of scale in urban life needs careful accumulation and review. In this the co-operation of business will be needed; there also must be more penetrating family cost-of-living data, geared to the various patterns of urban life.

These studies are called for not solely as an aid in developing

[20] Coleman Woodbury, "Economic Implications of Urban Growth," paper delivered at the meeting of the American Association for the Advancement of Science, December 1957; Gulick, *op. cit.*

[21] Stuart A. Rice, "Statistical Programming for Problems of Urban Agglomeration," paper delivered at the American Association for the Advancement of Science, December 1957.

sound conservation policies, designed for the new age of cities, but also to guide us in revising governmental structures, tax systems, and other social measures. Urbanism is now a fundamental factor of our life, and requires a far better foundation of knowledge for planning and for action than we have.

The second plan of action now called for is cultural and educational. It is right along the line which Resources for the Future and others have already been pursuing, but with certain new elements of emphasis. It proposes that we gather information, explore methods of formulation and communication, so that our rising generations, especially city boys and girls, may be more deeply conscious of their place in nature, and morally committed to a science-based conservation philosophy.

This is not as difficult as some may think. On the scientific side more research and experimentation *in this spirit* are required and can be provided. On the cultural and educational side, remember, most of our people came from lands where men loved and respected the soil and its resources. Mankind has a bad record with mining, especially since the runaway industrial revolution, and with the destructive grazing of goats around the Mediterranean and in the Near East. But except for this, most of our ancestors lived with dikes, sustained-yield forests, restricted grazing, terraces, fertilizers, land and water use regulation and soil conservation practices, geared to the *flow of nature,* not to its sudden exhaustion. Is there any reason why we cannot build these concepts with, of course, a more scientific basis, back again into our basic mores? It took less than two generations for the early settlers to become morally and spiritually, as well as practically, committed to the words and dogmas of democracy even in the face of conflicting self-interest. It takes but two decades to fit rural children into urban, industrial, commercial, and professional life. Why should it take any longer to make the responsible use of resources a fixed principle of American life, once the doctrine is adequately formulated in modern terms, and our educational, political, and spiritual leadership have the material with which to work? A people which boasts universal education, teachers' colleges, radio and TV saturation, a free press, applied psychology, and

Madison Avenue should have no difficulty in building a valid new idea into our fundamental culture within a single generation.

Something also needs to be said about the governmental and administrative task. Without organized action, things don't happen according to rational plans in a complex social and economic world, where men live elbow to elbow. The bulk of this action will be personal, voluntary, and corporate, based on human beliefs and spiritual commitments. But in dealing with the conservation of natural resources and the maintenance of a general policy of drawing down current production rather than capital resources, there must be also a broad framework of conscious and authoritative social control. This is government action. It involves the determination of policies in words after debate and compromise—that is legislation; it involves enforcement and management—that is the executive function; and it involves the settlement of individual grievances and broad interpretations of law through independent courts.

The essential thing here, as we have learned in other fields, is to identify the few key things that must be rationalized or regulated and to set the action priorities, so that we may leave the bulk of life and action to free enterprise, and still achieve the goals we seek.

As to the problems identified earlier as arising primarily out of the new pressures of urbanization on our resources, this approach suggests that there are now four matters for priority action, without even waiting for extensive research.

These are allocating water resources, eliminating flood dangers and water pollution, reserving open spaces, and controlling the general pattern of land use particularly around metropolitan regions and thruway interchanges. These last tasks must be related to the total circulation pattern, i.e., transportation, a matter I am not discussing in this paper.

These are the four key factors I would identify as now calling for containment. If the American people will take a firm hold of water, open spaces, air pollution, and the land use pattern around the urban centers, they will be able to bring urbanization into reasonable and rational balance with the major national resources we have identified.

It is not possible in this paper to discuss at all fully the type of action required for each of these four key subjects, and the appropriate division of the work among the federal government, the states and the local governments. However, a few observations are in order.

First of all, nothing is gained by belittling the extent of government action called for. In certain fields of life, notably land and resource management, it is necessary and normal for government to set the general framework and fix the rules of the game. This statement rests solidly on three thousand years of human experience.

Second, once this has been done, we can rely heavily on pricing and the market mechanism to determine interrelations, priorities, and comparative needs and desires. This statement rests on solid American experience. But, as to major resources and the general pattern of urbanized land uses, there must be public action to set the conditions before private enterprise is turned loose to work out the further details of development.

Third, let us never forget that the problems with which we are dealing are not primarily engineering and administrative matters. They are questions of fundamental long-range social policy. They are the stuff of politics.

The controls we are talking about go to the root of our society and its structure of power. We are dealing with who gets what, when and how, to use Harold Lasswell's pragmatic definition of politics. What we are saying is that the growth of urbanism has now raised these resource matters to the level of imperative public interest. It is this which justifies and requires governmental action.

It follows also that governmental action in these matters must be taken under the determination of our democratic political institutions. The powers we are talking about cannot be assigned solely to technicians, planners, independent authorities, or bureaucrats. The only way to proceed is through responsible political action, under the guidance of political leadership. The experts could probably move more quickly and do a better job at the start than is to be expected through our political machinery. Professional help surely will be needed all along the line. But little fundamental will be done and *made to stick* unless it is done as a matter of national, state, and local political commitment through our normal democratic channels.

This is the reason I place such stress on public education and the raising up of boys and girls, and men and women, who are morally committed to the conservation goals of urban society. It is this understanding and moral commitment which equips them to discharge their political responsibilities.

Finally, in our federal system of government, with distinct levels which are national, state, and local, the new work we are talking about must be appropriately divided among these three levels.

In doing this we must note that these jobs need not be handed to levels of government in solid functional blocks, assigning all water problems to one level, all land controls to another, all open space problems to another, and so forth. Each of these functions needs to be divided into its national, its regional, its local *aspects* so that these aspects may be appropriately assigned so as to fit into other political and administrative assignments. Obviously the broadest allocation of resources and the control of pollution on interstate rivers and harbors is a national or regional problem; but the distribution of water to the individual consumers can best be a local operation. Similarly, the broader land-use allocations must be regional, not local, while the control of the filling-in developments can best be local, not regional.

As an example, take the big problems of traffic around the great cities. The planning department is within the city. But the greatest need for planning is in the periphery, where there either is no political structure that can plan, or else local parochial planning so tied to a narrow interest of small communities that there is no base for sound results.

We need to create in the United States some broader bases of comprehensive thinking. While it is a wonderful thing to break bottlenecks by having one group build water systems, another group build highway systems, another one build bridges, and so on, it is also desirable to have these activities interrelated. And that condition can be achieved only by using governmental units that cover a bigger regional area.

It is also possible to separate the planning functions from the control or construction operations. We do this already when we separate policy, or legislative, aspects from enforcement, or executive and judicial operations. But I would caution against thinking that planning can be done in a vacuum by those who have no responsibility for action or too narrow a base of operations. It is equally dangerous to permit action agencies to operate over these areas without professional planning divisions. However, planning as a functionalized activity need not all be at one level, as planning too can be split into its over-all aspects, its regional aspects, and its local aspects, provided we learn how to interrelate the broader and the narrower processes so as to keep the broad plans realistic, and the local plans consistent.

This is not the occasion for fuller elaboration of these political and administrative questions. I have sought here only to indicate that the problems can be solved within the framework of our cultural, economic, and political systems.

It may even be found that a combination of such institutions— governmental, economic, and cultural—will lead ultimately to an adjustment of population size to fit consumption and space-use levels in conformity with the flow-of-nature policy, thus protecting mankind indefinitely against the dire predictions of Malthus or of Darwin or, most recently, of Paul B. Sears.[22] Under such an approach, mankind would achieve a dynamic stability at a level consistent with the good life, rather than at a level of increasing degradation.

We may take great comfort also from another thought. It is this: beginning with the year 2000 A.D. or thereabouts, in the United States, the improvement of living standards for the great masses of the population will not involve more physical consumption per capita, but will involve the unending advancement of cultural, social, and spiritual standards. From that point on, we will measure "progress" not by the increase of milk, meat, steel, electricity, gasoline, and cement consumed, but by the growing development of technical services, the increased enjoyment of leisure, sports, and the creative arts, and the indices of educational, intellectual, and spiritual life. And these activities, we need not emphasize, take very little more pulp, power, and produce than now goes into lesser levels of occupation, entertainment, and the various tranquilizers.

As we think and argue about water, land, air, energy, open spaces, and other resources separately, and I hope wisely, we can never

[22] Paul B. Sears, "The Inexorable Problem of Space," *Science,* Vol. 127, No. 3288 (January 1958).

forget that man, including urban man, must always move and live and have his being in his total environment, not separately in each of the neat cubbyholes which the experts have laid out to facilitate technical analysis.

Except in his own eyes, and we hope in the eyes of the Creator, man is just another animal, albeit a social animal.

In any case, man occupies his habitat and can exist, can prosper, can multiply only as he fits the total environment. And when man modifies this environment with his clever hands and inventive brain, he introduces new equilibria, ever-changing like a kaleidoscope, the end results of which may be less hospitable to the human species than the "balance of nature" within which man started his long climb to knowledge and power.

For this reason, mankind needs to proceed with due modesty, forever exploring the interrelatedness of his world and devoting his ingenuity and creative talents more to living within the flow of nature than upon the accumulated resources of his planet.

While this precept of the life-balance system is for all of mankind, it is of special significance for metropolitan man now, not alone because of his more involved and heavier dependence on resources, but because his apparent detachment from nature leaves him aloof and insensitive to the life system of which he is forever a dependent part.

The shortage mankind needs to guard against is not the exhaustion of the limited resources on this small planet. The shortage to fear is the lack of brains, character, spirit, leadership, and political competence. The depletion of land, water, and other resources could bring the prodigal son back to his senses, but his salvation will be found only in cultural conversion and in the arts of politics.

Every day we postpone the appropriate research and the educational and political action now called for will make the problem more difficult. As Homer said, only yesterday, "It is not meet to stand here wasting our time or idly loitering, for there is still a great work to be done."

SOME PROBLEMS IN CITY PLANNING

✍ Joseph L. Intermaggio

Dr. Gulick has made a sweeping, penetrating, and eloquent analysis of urban growth and its impact on natural resources. He states the major problems confronting our urban-industrial society as it expands to meet the needs of an increasing population that is reaching new income levels in economic life and making new demands on our technology. Also, he offers some provocative suggestions about ways to deal with the consequences of expanding urbanization.

It is refreshing to hear problems discussed in such a buoyant spirit. This no doubt derives from his broad perspective and confidence in the future; nowhere does Dr. Gulick appear to be overly concerned about the magnitude of the difficulties to be overcome in bringing about the required solutions. In fact, he predicts an "unending advance of cultural, social, and spiritual standards."

There are no indignant indictments of the causes of the present condition of our congested and deteriorating cities, although he

JOSEPH INTERMAGGIO is Project Director of the Committee on Urban Research of the National Academy of Sciences—National Research Council. A city planner by training, Mr. Intermaggio was previously Chief Planner of Arlington County, Virginia. Recently he was a planner and participant in the symposium of the Connecticut General Life Insurance Company, "New Highways: Challenge of the Metropolitan Regions"; and in the fall of 1957 was a planner with the *Fortune* and *Architectural Forum* workshop on open spaces. He was born in Brooklyn, N. Y., in 1915, and received his master's in regional planning in 1952 from Cornell University.

138

would have been thoroughly justified in reciting the price of past spoliation of resources. His is a sober call to reason through our problems and, through a guiding social and economic policy, to apply our skills to achieve higher social ends.

Dr. Gulick's paper has special qualities that appeal to me. It has unity; the physical, environmental, social, and governmental aspects of the problems are interrelated. And throughout, one senses his regard for people. This paper is so provocative and covers so broad a range that I can comment here on only a few of the many points worthy of further discussion and analysis.

Dr. Gulick does leave out one key point that I would like to stress —the unnecessary drain on our resources caused by progressive deterioration of the urban areas. He refers only to the resources needed to meet future growth. Reginald Isaacs estimates that urban renewal will cost "almost two trillion dollars by 1970," and states further that:

> New demands will be placed upon resources already diminishing under the impact of high productivity; their use under the requirements of a full urban renewal treatment program will approach that of war years. For even longer range considerations, there is required education, policies, legislation and enforcement of conservation practices.[1]

It is difficult to isolate the specific impact of urbanism on our natural resources apart from the unique requirements of our industrial technology, except insofar as the people concentrated in urban areas make special demands on land and on water, and affect air and water by their activities. Let us examine several of the examples cited.

As Dr. Gulick indicates, urban water needs are the result of the concentration of industry and of consumers. Water needs in the United States are expected to increase by 150 per cent over the next two or three decades, for which industry will account for 95 per cent.[2] It may be good that water shortages may in some instances

[1] Reginald R. Isaacs, "The Real Costs of Urban Renewal," *Problems of United States Economic Development* (New York: Committee for Economic Development), I, 1958.

[2] J. Frederic Dewhurst and Associates, *America's Needs and Resources* (New York: Twentieth Century Fund, 1955), p. 943.

restrain urbanization by limiting industrial development; the result may well be more rational industrial, and hence urban, patterns.

Dr. Gulick wisely recognizes that, in some regions of rapid recent growth, even conservation and ingenuity have their limits. The promise of demineralization of salt water no one can yet evaluate.

Pollution is discussed as a cause of resource waste. Air, water, and ground pollution, and dumping, are not fairly assignable to urban areas for, even though the cities are the chief offenders, many of their activities are carried on for the whole economy. The real culprit is the absence of effective use of technology available to control pollution. Moreover, these problems are soluble, no matter what their dimensions. This is a problem of political dynamics and of the willingness of the public authorities to deal effectively with the cause of pollution, whatever it may be. Public controls must be used to prevent overloading; technology must be used to correct pollution that has already reached the danger point. This includes controlling exhausts from automobiles and diesel trains, trucks and buses which, in some cities, are making the air as intolerable as smoke from uncontrolled industrial sources.

As for ground pollution, in some places fine homes are already surrounded by continually overflowing cesspools and septic fields. In some communities the ground itself has become saturated. Yet new subdivisions are being added that have no sewers. Like water and air pollution, the problem of ground pollution is soluble. But taking action means obtaining the large financial resources to do the job. Of the financial problems involved, Dr. Gulick is well aware.

Energy consumption per capita is higher in urban regions, again, not only because of the nature of urban development, but also because industry is concentrated there. Our energy resources have proved far more adequate than previous forecasters believed possible. A major factor has been the growing efficiency of energy production.[3] Advancing technology and new sources of fuel, developed and potential, would appear to offer reasonable hope that the energy demands of our urban centers will continue to be adequately met.

Dr. Gulick asserts that because urban incomes are higher, urban dwellers consume more nonrenewable resources. This is a proposi-

[3] Dewhurst, *op. cit.*

tion of doubtful validity. I agree with him that "we cannot prove fully, or balance out satisfactorily and finally the scale factors involved in urbanization." It seems that much of the higher income in cities is spent for increased costs of housing, food, and service. No unusual use of resources appears to be involved here. Furthermore, a substantial part of urban taxes taken out of higher urban income is used to provide for nonurban needs.

Recreation needs are not generated by urban development. They arise out of the whole pattern of income, technology, and leisure time. Dr. Gulick makes a good summary of this problem, "the growing urban regions, with their expanding economic activities . . . will need and demand more acres of open space within easy reach, more resources for wide, uncrowded, free re-creation of bodies, minds, and spirits."

Recreation must be viewed as a conservation measure of human resources, not as a consumer of natural resources. Our present recreation resources *are* grossly underdeveloped and for the city dweller too distant and often accessible only on vacation. We just need more parks, as Dr. Gulick points out. Yet many potential recreation areas—our beaches, woodlands, lakefronts, and stream valleys—are still being pre-empted for commercial, industrial, and housing developments. In our concern for the preservation of the natural resources of the nation, the relative availability of open space for the crowded urban dweller of moderate means also must be considered.

Dr. Gulick describes the need to develop "new concepts of recreation . . . matched to urban life and the changing age pattern of our people." While I was glad to see the suggestion to fill some of this need "in the confines of the urban design itself," only the planned development of urban regions offers opportunities to integrate recreation needs with other essential needs. The pressure on existing recreation facilities will be relieved to the extent that the potential demand is distributed.

For our growing population no alternative is offered to the extension of the urban areas. We are not developing satellite cities and towns. The most serious aspect of this problem is the encroachment on desirable agricultural land having unique qualities. Although all the metropolitan areas combined occupy only 7 per cent of the total land area of the United States, the effect of their expansion into good agricultural land is enormous. This underscores the need for an adequate national land use survey. Whatever the economic or cultural losses may be, equally serious is the lost opportunity to create a satisfactory design for the urban region. As Dr. Gulick states, "urbanization does increase the pressure on land as a resource, and accentuates the need for planned controls and for dynamic programs of land conservation and use."

In the second part of his paper, Dr. Gulick makes proposals to deal with the increased pressures on our resources. I concur that we need more scientific analyses of the impact of urbanization on our resources if a sound public and private policy is to be developed. We need (1) to establish a firm basis for policy decisions about the character of regional development; (2) to program public works for conservation of resources and for economic development; and (3) to adopt measures for renewal, conservation, and rehabilitation of cities, and for the building of new cities.

Our social science research effort also needs to be expanded if decisions about the character of future urbanization is to be realistically adapted to changing needs.

Dr. Gulick has made an admirable argument for education in resource use. Americans have not yet grasped the full extent of our urban problems, nor have enough dedicated persons become concerned with them. As Father Hesburgh has said, what happens to education, happens to America.[4] I, too, believe that our schools, with inspired teachers, could bring about a revival in our sense of values and in the sense of community that underlies any successful social and political program.

Dr. Gulick's statement of the role of government and its relation to private action is succinct. Without the broad framework of conscious and authoritative social control he suggests, no program will succeed.

The few elements for priority action at first seem to oversimplify the task—but actually they are comprehensive. If air, water, land, and transportation are controlled adequately in interrelated programs

[4] Father Theodore Hesburgh, University of Notre Dame, on CBS program, "The Great Challenge: Education for What," February 23, 1958.

based on common policy, then a firm basis will exist for bringing urbanization into a reasonable and rational balance with the major natural resources.

Dr. Gulick makes a masterful statement of the government action that is needed. This is the credo of a man who has confidence in his fellow man, a faith in the fruits of education that lead to understanding, and a conviction that democratic institutions resting on a sure foundation of an articulate citizenry can invent and carry out effective solutions to problems that affect the community.

Being a resident of Virginia in these times, I am constantly reminded of the vast gap between our technological progress and our progress in government and institutions in the last 150 years. Of course this is precisely the stumbling block to effective solutions to our urgent problems. This difficulty makes it even more imperative that the education effort be vigorous.

Broad corroboration of the points of view in Dr. Gulick's conclusion, with its exhortation that we use our intellects and resources creatively, is found in the statement of Lewis Mumford, who said:

> We have now reached a point where these fresh accumulations of historical insight and scientific knowledge are ready to flow over into social life, to mold anew the forms of cities, to assist in the transformation of both the instruments and the goals of our civilization.[5]

A comparable view was expressed by Dr. Detlev Bronk:

> It is not enough for this country to be pre-eminent in the natural sciences. We must match scientific progress with the further development of all forms of creative effort in order to achieve the more satisfying life that our economy and technology are capable of providing.[6]

Dr. Gulick has enriched our resources of ideas and understanding. I hope the nation will match his ideas with action.

[5] Lewis Mumford, *The Culture of Cities* (New York: Harcourt, Brace and Co., 1938), p. 10.

[6] Detlev W. Bronk in foreword of brochure, *Committee on Urban Research* (Washington: National Academy of Sciences—National Research Council, 1957).

OUR NEED OF BREATHING SPACE

Sigurd F. Olson

The urban sprawl is here to stay; it will continue and increase in the foreseeable future. Anyone who has flown over the United States during the past few years cannot help but be impressed with the evidence of this movement into the countryside. This growth is especially dramatic when flying at night, when cities and their radiating arteries of traffic look like skeins of Christmas tree lights, giant flowing tentacles reaching out into the dark, probing farther and farther into the surrounding land. There was a time not very long ago when you could leave the glow of metropolitan centers behind, but today, especially in the eastern half of the country, one barely leaves one glow before being conscious of another in the distance.

Nor is there any question but that this urban development exerts a great drain on natural resources. Luther Gulick has pointed out

---

SIGURD F. OLSON is President of the National Parks Association, Wilderness Ecologist for the Izaak Walton League of America, consultant to the President's Quetico-Superior Committee, former Dean of Ely Junior College, Ely, Minnesota. These formal designations, however, tell very little of a man who has devoted most of his life to the preservation of wilderness regions all over the continent, who has led many expeditions by canoe in the Quetico-Superior and the far northwest where he is known as Bourgeois, the French Canadians' name for leaders of treks into the remote hinterlands in the early days of exploration and trade. Among his writings, *The Singing Wilderness* is perhaps the best known. Another book, "Listening Point," is to be published soon. He was born in Chicago in 1899 and received degrees at the universities of Wisconsin and Illinois.

graphically what a high standard of living has done, what metropolitan services mean in terms of natural resources use, the attendant results in terms of air and water pollution, energy consumption, flood control, the use of the land itself and its ultimate removal from any use but that of real estate. It is in this respect particularly that I would like to supplement some of his ideas.

He states, "We will need more acres of open space within easy reach . . . totally new concepts of recreation . . . active programs for some, contemplative opportunities for many, and glimpses of beauty for all."

I could not agree more wholeheartedly, and I challenge anyone to contest the importance of these objectives. The great question, however, is how to reach them.

Dr. Gulick says further that ultimately urbanization will make possible the true conservation of the land. This is entirely possible, but with the type of uncontrolled and unplanned development now going on, it is highly improbable. We might come near to realizing the possibilities if we could regulate the nature and character of the extension of cities; if we could confine the growth within reasonable limits. But until we do, urbanization in its present form is a threat not only to our economy but to our physical and spiritual welfare. In the interim all we can hope for is to sandbag the flood wherever we can, hoping that eventually the high waters will subside of their own accord.

The inference that population growth will eventually be controlled by the attainment of an even higher material standard of living than we now enjoy, and a higher cultural level, and that through them population pressures may be brought into a far better ecological balance than most Malthusian predictions postulate, also seems doubtful to me. Certainly there is no sign in the postwar generation that a high standard of living is inducing social, political, and fundamental cultural attitudes that will bring about a better ecological adjustment.

Inasmuch as the dream of most urban dwellers is to get into the country, and industrial developments are moving out as well, this trend is bound to continue. The urge behind all of this is not new to Americans. We are a people who, until recently, lived close to the soil. Coming from pioneer and immigrant stock, many of us from farms and small towns, we have deep within us the feel of the frontier and the so-called "good old days," the feel of living and, if possible, working away from congestion and city sights and sounds and smells. While few urban dwellers would want to exchange their way of living for the past, there is a definite nostalgia, not only evidenced by the urban growth into the open country, but by the tremendous increase in recreational travel, the fifty-odd million going into our national parks annually, the demand for camping, hunting, and fishing opportunities.

Ask the average city dweller what he thinks is the ideal life, and what might contribute to his greater happiness, and he will no doubt think of possibly another car, a bigger TV screen, a longer vacation, and less traffic to contend with. Ask him if the American dream means the disappearance of little towns with shady streets, open countrysides, to be replaced by greater and greater industrialization with smoke stacks instead of trees, polluted air instead of the smells of fields and woods, gadgets and labor-saving devices replacing simplicity, with the feeling of the out-of-doors in his daily life becoming more and more a memory, and he will shrug his shoulders and wonder if you are slightly insane. Instead of the old music his forebears listened to, and the rhythms of nature and seasons which regulated their lives, he has listened so long to the drums of the Chambers of Commerce that the American dream has become synonymous with the goal of unlimited exploitation and economic growth.

While we have made great progress in developing knowledge of conservation during the past fifty years, we still are a long way from understanding and accepting Aldo Leopold's classic concept of an "ecological conscience," or as Dr. Gulick says, "an awareness on the part of urban man of his relationship to the world of nature."

I am not as sanguine as he as to what we can do about this. While it might be true, as Dr. Gulick suggests, that with our highly developed techniques of education and communication, "it should be possible to build a valid new idea into our fundamental culture within a generation or two," we all know that any educational program as broad and basic in its concepts as this, affecting as it ultimately must the entire basis of social planning as well as our mores, will take the kind of money, brains and organization, guidance and leadership that we now seem to be throwing into the arms race. Only with a similar sense of urgency, under dedicated and inspired leadership, can this be done. Only through education and subsequent government action can the problem be solved permanently. It will take an enormous effort and all the ingenuity we possess. The tragedy of the situation is that as yet there is no sense of urgency and no leadership that might bring about powerful governmental support and financing.

We are confronted with a situation where urban growth is so fast, changes coming so swiftly, that we cannot wait for the slow processes of education. New cities are mushrooming without any planning, great housing and industrial developments going on with no thought for breathing spaces, parks or recreational needs generally. Already the need is being felt in suburbia, but still there is no design, no city or community planning, the result being confusion and subsequent loss of social values. In the city of Washington there is even serious consideration of sacrificing park areas for expressways. The bulldozers of big contractors, real estate operators, and industrial engineers are dictating the shape of cities of the future and the way a people must live. There is no thought of living "in the flow of nature." Urban man has thrown plans to the winds and is living a catch-as-catch-can existence dominated by impermanence, speed, and fluidity of movement. He is divorcing himself from the earth, and in this divorcement he is losing contact with elemental and spiritual things, his sense of oneness with his environment, psychological and physiological needs for which he has been conditioned for a million years by an entirely different existence. Ecological adjustments and adaptations take aeons of time. They do not take place in the short space of a few generations. Man is not yet ready for a capsule existence in a highly organized and artificial world, removed from the privilege of living close to the earth and experiencing the forces of nature and living in harmony with them.

It is wonderful to have national parks and forests to go to, but they are not enough. It is not enough to make a trip once a year or to see these places occasionally over a long week-end. We need to have places close at hand, breathing spaces in cities and towns, little plots of ground where things have not changed; green belts, oases among the piles of steel and stone. Children especially need this contact, for they have not as yet been weaned from the primal needs of the race. We need, in addition to such places, some areas large enough to be set aside as wilderness, where there is no design, no planning whatsoever, no management of plants or animals, where people may sense what this planet was like before man achieved the power of revamping it for his needs. Such regions, while they might seem to have no economic use, would act as buffers to a civilization that might destroy man's equilibrium and sanity. It is perhaps not without reason that Thoreau said, "In wildness is the preservation of the world."

In John Kenneth Galbraith's discussion of the economics of natural resources he implied that conservationists were so concerned with preserving isolated wilderness regions that they could not see the importance of controlling such blights as billboards along our highways. His statement indicated a lack of understanding of what conservation as a movement really means. While the control of billboards is a challenge to "Keeping America Beautiful," it cannot be considered in the same category with the broad aspects of soil, water, forests, and wildlife, the preservation of recreational areas, or unrenewable resources which can never be replaced—matters that have to do with the very basis of our culture and richness of living. While economics are important, it must be remembered that unless resources are preserved there will be nothing for economists to work with. With respect to urban developments, if planning does not now result in the setting aside of breathing spaces, planners of the future will be confronted with a frozen, crystallized situation where human needs can be satisfied only through enormous expense and physical difficulty.

Dr. Gulick says, "It may be found that a combination of governmental, economic, and cultural institutions will lead to an adjustment of population to fit consumption and space use levels in conformity with the flow-of-nature policy."

Such a utopia is highly desired and I do not say it cannot be achieved, but in the light of our attitude, our preoccupation with material things, the character of our mushrooming civilization, it is highly improbable that it can come about early enough to save the situation before we are forced to face the problems that determined a way of life in the Middle East. There is no alternative today. We must move into this vacuum without all of the preliminaries of preparation, move swiftly with courage and vision, confident that the future will prove the wisdom of our action.

This is a difficult thing to do in a democratic system. We must stop talking about natural resources, recreational areas, and conservation generally in cold-blooded economic terms, seeing them only as graphs and statistics, national income and expenditures, taxes, price supports and programs. We must see them from an ecological point of view involved with such inherent needs as freedom, human dignity, and happiness. We must recognize the human necessity of keeping physical contact with the land, knowing now and in the generations to come the meaning of the old simplicities and satisfactions. While we may well be able to provide synthetics in fuel, food, and materials to take the place of exhausted resources of the past, cope with an expanding population without starvation or want, the great question will always be: Is this enough, is this the kind of a world we really want to live in?

Once having decided what we want and recognizing that there is no time to waste, no time to wait for the orderly and logical results of an educational program extending across decades, the question before us is: What can and what must be done now? The answer is first of all to find the leadership, and then for city, state, and federal governments to move immediately into the field of natural resources, doing everything possible to bring them into adjustment with consumption. While there is still time, governments must also attempt to plan urban developments so that recreational areas of all kinds are set aside to meet the needs of a burgeoning population. It makes little difference what the immediate designations of such reservations may be. The important thing is to acquire and preserve them before they are gone forever. At the most, we have a decade to accomplish this purpose. If we wait much longer than that at the rate we are building now, the land will be gone and our opportunity for the future as well.

SELECTIVE OPPORTUNISM,
THE SUREST WAY

✍ *Abel Wolman*

Dr. Gulick adds another dramatic exposition of the characteristics and problems of urban explosion to the already overflowing series of diagnostic and epidemiologic reviews of this prime headache of modern society. Although he refers to this phenomenon as new (a view which I have), he views it primarily as peculiar to this country. The phenomenon is, of course, universal in impact, whether in London, Paris, Bangkok, Tokyo, Hongkong, or Manila.

Throughout the world, people flock to the urban centers for presumed opportunities for a better life. They surround the old core cities with amorphous, unco-ordinated, inadequately serviced incubators for the worst slums of the not too distant future. Dr. Gulick succinctly summarizes the resultant pressures and problems of these modern sequels of population growth. They bring demands for higher

---

A B E L   W O L M A N , Professor of Sanitary Engineering at Johns Hopkins University, is Chairman of the permanent Committee of Sanitary Engineers for the Pan American Sanitary Bureau. He is Chairman of the Sanitary Engineering Committee of the Division of Medical Sciences, National Research Council; former Chief Engineer of the Department of Health of Maryland; and has been consulting engineer to such organizations as the City of Baltimore, the United States Public Health Service, TVA, Atomic Energy Commission, and the Army. Professor Wolman has also been president of the American Water Works Association and is a former president of the American Public Health Association. He was born in Baltimore, Maryland, in 1892, and received his degree in engineering from Johns Hopkins University in 1915.

consumption standards and new patterns of settlement and life. He does a service in focusing discussion upon the impact of this behavior on resources, particularly upon water, air, energy, floods, wastes, recreation and relaxation, and land use. In virtually every case, this impact means higher costs.

Where he reaches the crux of the problem, namely, "what can be done about it?" he and most other contributors to this scene fail us! No one is so naive as to believe that there is a slide-rule answer to this question. It is undoubtedly true that answers will be geologically slow in time, fumbling, and lacking in perfection.

Perhaps it would be useful to drag out from beneath the pregnant philosophical proposals Dr. Gulick so wisely presents, some of the missing links in action which past experience discloses. Every conservationist, planner, and observant citizen needs to take these to heart in programming next steps.

One of the striking features of the past twenty years is that general planning in urban sprawl is just too slow to keep up with the tempo of action on all fronts. It may be unfortunately true, as some cynical observer has recently said, that "planning is catching up with the inevitable!" If it is even partially true, perhaps the force of the planner might be greatly strengthened if his emphasis were on the broad guidance of growth and less on the detail; if perfectionism were less a restraint and more of an ultimate goal; if intrusion into the action group decisions were more persuasive, more militant, and less abstract. Unless these moves and shifts in perspective are prompt, and some are almost already too late, the developments in highway construction, housing, zoning, urban renewal, and mass transport will bring a long train of sadness in their wake over the next two decades.

A similar dilemma confronts us in the development of the necessary political structure for managing the resources requirements and uses in metropolitan areas. The struggle between two schools of thought is also apparent here. The perfectionist seeks all-purpose government. The opportunist moves to ad hoc improvisation for those functions most easily consolidated, without hurdling the antagonisms, jealousies and fears of disparate groups. It must be confessed that those who wait for the millennium of all-purpose government are likely to be disappointed. More important, in the meantime they fail to influence action even if only on a piecemeal basis. In essence, one is often driven to choose the better of several realistic compromises.

The leisurely process of diagnosis, appraisal, discussion, and proposals for unification of government in the Washington metropolitan area is an example of this indoor and outdoor sport. While we attempt to knit two states and the District of Columbia, numerous counties, and dozens of municipalities into a single super government, the procession of actionists moves forward with almost astronomic speed. How much better it would be to run forward with those devices, admittedly limited, which will bring some degree of planning sense and integration into the program.

Society furthermore must ultimately recognize that many decisions made within the last twenty years have driven us into programs creating artificial forms of living, drying up forever open spaces, developing housing abortions, and forcing social stratifications which will take years to undo. Some of my best friends appear at every zoning hearing to see to it that the unwelcome will be planned into my area instead of theirs. Perhaps again such eventualities were inevitable, but now is the time to take stock of our "barracks philosophy" in relation to the program of public education which Dr. Gulick emphasizes.

This is an appropriate occasion also to recognize the pressing necessity for confronting ourselves with the fate of the core city—the nourishing mother of the urban sprawl. The city still remains the root of metropolitan living; a root often weakened with the benefit and blessing of the planning clergy. Have all the values of the city been adequately assessed, since it still remains the major firm tax base of the metropolis, supplies the sinews of work and commerce, and is the source of many of the resources, functions, and services upon which the metropolitan area draws?

It is not too late to place before the suburbanite the unpalatable truth that the city taxes which he wished to escape are more than matched by the costs of the "city-like" services which he now demands and requires. Dr. Gulick and others point out that services in suburbia are invariably more costly than in a city. Lot frontages per house are generally greater and distances for service lines, interceptor sewers, highways, energy wires are most often greater than for equivalent populations in the municipality. Since only the property tax is visible in suburbia, the other costs appear in less obtrusive disguises. They are all part of costs, however, which so far are ignored in perpetuating the myth of lower servicing costs and taxes in suburbia.

All these observations simply reinforce the actions suggested by Dr. Gulick in the last pages of his text. The pleas which I add are simply pleas for more speed of plan, more realism of participation in action, more rather than less improvisation, and far more militancy in public and private discussion of all of the functional issues so dramatically forced upon us by urbanization.

As is so often the case, these general observations were so much better stated some thirty years ago by the Committee on the Regional Plan of New York and its Environs, in the following terms:

> Generally speaking planning may be inspired by one of three policies. The two that are easiest to follow in planning for the future are, first, that practical policy which does not extend beyond the concrete and the present, and, second, that idealistic policy that is based solely on the abstract and the future. Under the former policy proposals are made to flow with the current created by established habits and vested interests; and under the second they are confined to what ought to be, without regard to the limits imposed by unalterable conditions. The one policy lacks soul, and the other flesh and blood, and those who follow them find planning a simple exercise.
>
> The third, which seeks an ideal based on realities—an ideal shaped by the processes of reason and not by the play of fancy—involves the greater labor but seems to present the only possibility for improving conditions of life and society. . . . An ideal, to be a worthy one, must be capable of being expressed in action; . . . To make an ideal real, we must believe it is a good thing to do, but also that it can be done. Because of this, a plan may appear to be of the highest quality in the sphere of what is attainable and yet of comparatively poor quality in the sphere of what is desirable in the abstract. Life offers ample scope for achievement within the realms of the practical, and greater satisfaction comes from conceiving the smaller things that can be done than in dreaming of the larger things that cannot be done.

NOTE BY DR. GULICK   There is no planner in America who has done more for the philosophical, unattainable, perfect solution of the major water resource distributions of the United States than Abel Wolman, who tells us that he is against it.

I am hopeful in the face of manifest impossibility because I have seen things done, and have participated in the doing of them. They have been done by getting the public sufficiently stirred up so that the politicians see what they call mileage. If you persuade them that there is mileage in a proposal, they will work with the planners and other people. One of the most important things that was accomplished by Mayor Wagner in reorganizing the government of the city of New York during this last four years was to take planning out of the distant ethereal blue and tie it in to the daily process of decision making. Every week when the Mayor's cabinet meets, the head planner participates. They don't always do what he says, but his thinking gets woven into the programing.

To make planning really effective you have to do several things at once. You have to build up a greater understanding, so that there is mileage in this. Then you have to overhaul the structure of organization so that the men who have the ability and the time and the technical staffs behind them to do the broader thinking can make their full contribution to the administrative decisions. In that way administrative decisions can be made in the light of technical competence and planning.

NOTE BY MR. WOLMAN   I am not against planning. I am *for* planning with high ingredients of realism, and planning that is conscious of a stream of life now.

V SOME DETERMINANTS OF RESOURCE POLICY

The Political Economy of Resource Use

EDWARD S. MASON

The Broadening Base of Resource Policy

ROBERT W. HARTLEY

Policy Criteria for Petroleum

MINOR S. JAMESON, JR.

The Waning Role of Laissez Faire

BUSHROD W. ALLIN

THE POLITICAL ECONOMY
OF RESOURCE USE

⚑ Edward S. Mason

The general subject of this whole book is the conservation of natural resources. Unfortunately, a commentator on conservation problems seems to be given a choice between a definition of conservation so broad as to be meaningless and one so narrow that it excludes most of the questions that have occupied conservationists. If conservation is defined as a "wise use of resources" nothing escapes its ken, but the invitation to subjective value judgments is so sweeping as to leave little room for rational analysis. If, on the other hand, conservation is defined as "a shift in the time distribution of the rate of use of a re-

EDWARD S. MASON, Dean of the Graduate School of Public Administration at Harvard University for the past eleven years, is well known for his versatility in the field of economics. Perhaps his greatest contributions, however, have centered in industrial organization, foreign economic policy, and international trade. He has been economic consultant to many branches of the United States Government, including the Department of Labor, the Defense Commission, and the Department of State. In 1947 he was appointed chief United States economic adviser to the Moscow conference on reparations. He was also a member of the President's Materials Policy Commission. More recently, at Harvard, he has been responsible for the establishment and conduct of the Economic Development Advisory Body to the Government of Pakistan Planning Board, and also for the establishment of the New York Metropolitan Regional Study. He was born in Clinton, Iowa, in 1899; received his B.Litt. from Oxford University, and his Ph.D. from Harvard University Graduate School.

157

source in the direction of the future," [1] we have a set of issues that can be analyzed, but one which represents only a small part of the traditional concern of conservationists. Rather than waste time at this juncture in the fruitless search for a definition that will both hospitably embrace the various views of conservationists, and at the same time represent a meaningful statement of a specific issue, I prefer to lay out a number of unresolved problems in what I have chosen to call the political economy of natural resource use.

My choice of "political economy" rather than economics obviously reflects a predilection for issues in the area of public policy. The term "problem" is here used in a public action context. Given a competitive price system in a free enterprise economy, will the use of natural resources roughly correspond to the use that, over time, will give the community the goods and services it might reasonably expect to have from these resources? If "laissez faire," or an unfettered price system, tends to produce conspicuous wastes in the use of resources there is, in my use of the word, a "problem," whose solution may require public intervention. The four areas I have chosen for discussion are all areas in which government intervention has, in fact, been extensive. Whether intervention has been, or is, justified in the public interest or whether it represents merely the pressure of special interests is, of course, the principal question at issue. Since these four areas cover a substantial part of what may properly be called the political economy of natural resource use, the treatment I propose to give them is, perforce, extensive rather than intensive.

1. It is argued that a market determination of prices is unlikely to produce an adequate investment in the discovery and development of new sources of mineral supply. It is a fact that the practice of offering incentives to the discovery of new mineral deposits goes back at least to the Middle Ages and that most, if not all, of the mineralized countries of the world currently subsidize, through tax or other incentives, mineral discovery. Is there anything in the unimpeded functioning of the price system that tends to produce an undesirably low investment in the discovery and development of mineral deposits and, consequently, justifies governmental subsidy of discovery operations?

[1] S. V. Ciriacy Wantrup, *Resource Conservation* (Berkeley: University of California Press, 1952), p. 51.

2. It is said that characteristic supply and demand inelasticities in the production and consumption of raw materials tend, under laissez faire, to produce a range of price variation that works great and unnecessary hardship on producers and consumers and hampers the attainment of ideal inputs in the natural resource area. In the case of internationally traded raw materials, this price volatility is alleged to create foreign exchange difficulties that seriously damage the network of world trade. Are the conditions of raw material production sufficiently different from those of other commodities to justify public intervention designed to dampen or modify excessive price fluctuations?

3. It is argued that natural resource use under laissez faire is likely to be accompanied by economies and diseconomies external to the producing unit but internal to the economy as a whole, that can only be captured or avoided by public action. External diseconomies in the piecemeal development of water resources may provide the justification for multi-purpose river valley development under public authority. External diseconomies in the individual exploitation of oil reserves may only be avoided by public regulation or compulsory co-ordination of individual activities. External economies and diseconomies are, of course, not limited to natural resource use but, as recent writers have pointed out, most of the examples discussed in the literature appear to fall in the natural resource area.[2] And there seems to be a reason for this.

4. It is said that an unregulated exploitation of natural resources will frequently lead to the sacrifice of high-priority future uses in favor of low-priority present uses. Oil that will be needed later for the production of high-octane gasoline may, if competitively exploited, be currently used for oiling roads. The unimpeded cultivation of Appalachian hillsides or the plowing up of western range lands may destroy for all time the topsoil needed later to feed our growing population. According to this contention, laissez faire tends to produce waste in the form of a faulty time distribution in the use of our resources.

Two of these problem areas, the third and fourth, were central to the range of interests of the early conservationists and have remained

[2] *Cf.* Tibor Scitovsky, "Two Concepts of External Economies," *Journal of Political Economy,* April 1954.

a persistent concern of their followers. The Geological Survey as early as the 1890's was emphasizing the advantages of multi-purpose river valley development as against the nearly exclusive concern of the Corps of Engineers with the use of rivers for transportation. Gifford Pinchot in the Bureau of Forestry preached the doctrine of sustained yield forestry on private operations and later advocated enclosure into national forests as the best means of assuring a proper time distribution of the rate of cutting. The external diseconomies of competitive grazing and the sacrifice of future benefits through overgrazing impressed contemporary shapers of United States range land policy. An able historian of the conservation movement states that, "Roosevelt, Pinchot, Newell and others gradually recognized that underlying their former resource policies was a common thread of waste elimination and long-range planning." [3] And the wastes that principally engaged their attention were what are here called external diseconomies (or the neglect of possible external economies) and a faulty time distribution of the rate of use.

The conservation movement, to be sure, as a socio-political phenomenon, quickly broadened out to embrace much more, including public health, conservation of the morals of youth, elimination of child labor, preservation of natural beauty, "the elimination of waste in education and war, the conservation of manhood, and the conservation of the Anglo-Saxon race." [4] Pinchot campaigned for the Senate in 1914, on a platform of the conservation of human rights, natural resources, human welfare, and citizenship. A glance at the character and qualifications of the individuals and groups invited to the Conference on Resources for the Future in 1953 indicates how amorphous and undefined conservation, in the popular usage, has become. As President Taft earlier said, with some justice: there are a great many people in favor of conservation, no matter what it means.

At the core, however, conservation has always been primarily concerned with natural resources and with the possibilities of eliminating waste in natural resource use through government intervention. This seems to be the meaning favored in many state and federal statutes

[3] S. P. Hays, "The First American Conservation Movement, 1891–1920" (Ph.D. thesis, Harvard University, 1953), p. 201.
[4] *Ibid.*, p. 302.

regulating the use of natural resources in the interests of conservation. These statutes fairly firmly identify conservation as the avoidance of waste—any kind of waste. In the words of the Texas oil and gas conservation laws, "The production, storage or transportation of crude petroleum oil or natural gas in such a manner, in such amount, or under such conditions as to constitute waste is hereby declared to be unlawful and is prohibited." [5]

If, however, we push this notion of waste avoidance to its ultimate conclusion the concept of conservation becomes very broad indeed. To conserve would mean to economize and the theory of conservation becomes the theory of ideal output. Or rather, since methods of production as well as quantities of output are at issue, it becomes the theory of ideal inputs with its central concern an optimum allocation of resources among various uses. If the term is to be used this way it may properly be asked why conservation has any particular relevance to natural resource problems.

Considerations of this sort have led economists to favor a much narrower definition of conservation, one that is solely concerned with the time pattern of resource use. One of the leading economic authorities, Ciriacy Wantrup, defines conservation as a "redistribution of use in the direction of the future." Its opposite, depletion, he defines as redistribution "in the direction of the present." [6] If this definition is accepted, it is clear that a decision to conserve, i.e., to orient consumption toward the future, may be wasteful and that a decision to deplete may be economical. A shift in use rates in the direction of the future could increase costs, either private or social, by more than benefits are increased, and a shift in use rates toward the present could do the reverse. Ciriacy says as much: "The concepts 'conservation,' 'depletion,' and 'state of conservation' carry no connotation of efficiency or waste." [7]

This is a perfectly defensible use of terms. But to me it does violence to the ordinary usage of language. Conservation, outside as well as within the conservation movement, is a "good thing." It involves choosing the better course of action and rejecting the worse. As I shall

[5] Acts 1934, 44th Legislature, Laws of Texas, Chap. 76, Sec. 2, Article 6014.
[6] S. V. Ciriacy Wantrup, *op. cit.,* p. 51.
[7] *Ibid.,* p. 53.

use the term, therefore, it is a particular kind of economizing—the avoidance of wastes associated with a faulty time distribution of the use of resources. So used, the term is obviously not "objective" or *wertfrei;* value judgments are of the essence of conservation policy. And the values of a private planning agent are not necessarily the same as those of the government.

So much for definition. There seems little point in arguing further the merits of a broad versus a narrow meaning of conservation. I prefer the narrow meaning, and the fourth problem area I shall discuss deals with conservation in this sense. If conservation is defined as the avoidance of waste in natural resource use, a discussion of all four of my "problems" is relevant.

Subsidies to Mineral Discovery and Development

Most countries with important mineral deposits subsidize, in one way or another, discovery and development activity. The United States offers powerful tax inducements in the form of depletion allowances and the "expensing" of discovery and development costs. Special incentives are also offered to small discovery enterprises. Canada has somewhat lower depletion allowances but grants a three and one-half year exemption from income taxation to new producing properties.

What is at issue here is not a policy, motivated by security considerations, of granting special inducement, limited in time, to producers of strategic materials at home or abroad. We are not concerned with guaranteed prices, special development contracts, premium pricing, and all the other devices used during and, to some extent, after the war to stimulate production of materials for military use. These were short-term measures designed to meet a special problem. Our concern is with the continuing special advantages given to mineral exploration and production on the ground, apparently, that, without subsidy, investment and output in the minerals field will fall substantially short of what is desired.

The term "subsidy," of course, is a kind of swear word in the American business community, which is strange considering the universality of the phenomenon. But manufacturers whose domestic production is subsidized by tariff protection and farmers whose prices are supported by government action are equally vehement in rejecting the term "subsidy." In partial support of this attitude it must be admitted that it is excessively difficult to lay down any general operational definition that would permit us easily to distinguish subsidized from unsubsidized economic activities.[8] In the tax area the key notion is more favorable treatment for a particular group than is accorded to other taxpayers—farms or households—in the same class. But what is the same class? For mineral producers the question would appear to be whether percentage depletion is more favorable treatment than is accorded to, say, manufacturers through depreciation allowances limited to the cost of their assets. This raises a central question of natural resource economics here at issue. Are the conditions of mineral discovery and production so different from other types of production as to require special analysis and special treatment?

It is certainly not possible to determine the existence or extent of mineral subsidy by looking at the returns to factors employed. If our competitive system works the way it should, the effect of a subsidy to mineral production would be to expand investment and output—thus bringing down mineral prices—to the point at which the yield in mineral investments, taking full account of risks, is approximately equal to yields elsewhere. The objective test of the subsidy would presumably lie in a comparison of the current amount of investment and output with what they would have been in the absence of a subsidy. This, obviously, is a difficult comparison to make.[9]

In the special case of oil, the subsidy element in percentage depletion does not lead necessarily to an expansion of output since the Texas Railway Commission is always there to "adjust supply to de-

[8] *Cf.* Carl Kaysen, "On Defining a Subsidy" in *Public Policy,* a yearbook of the Harvard Graduate School of Public Administration, IV, 1953.

[9] But Arnold C. Harberger, comparing the relation between investment and value of output in the mineral, as against other industries, concludes that tax incentives "lead to a situation in which it takes $2 million of capital invested in mineral exploration to produce as much product as $1 million of capital invested in other industries." This would be possible only if the government bears a substantial part of the investment cost in the form of tax abatement, i.e., subsidy. *Cf.* Arnold C. Harberger, "The Taxation of Mineral Industries" in *Federal Tax Policy for Economic Growth and Stability.* Joint Committee of the Economic Report, 84th Congress, 1st Session, 1955.

mand." The character and amount of subsidy to oil production in the United States can only be understood in terms of the combined operations of percentage depletion, expensing of drilling operations, federal tax rates, state regulation of output, and limitation of imports. Even this formidable combination, however, need not produce an exceptionally high return to factors committed to oil production. It may merely mean that oil producers pay wildcatters a much higher price for oil discoveries than they would otherwise pay and both wildcatters and established oil producers are led to explore areas that would, in the absence of a high and stable price for oil, be left unexplored. Again the objective test of the nature and extent of the subsidy would lie in a comparison of the current investment in discovery with what the investment would be without percentage depletion, regulation of output, and import limitation. That this difference would be substantial there can be no doubt. But how much the difference is, no one knows.

Some light can be thrown on this matter by looking at the question historically. What was the purpose of the special treatment and how did its beneficiaries react? Was it to offer rewards to mineral discoverers commensurate with their special risks or, perhaps, in excess of these risks? And no doubt a careful study of the reactions of producers and of the returns to factors during the period of adjustment to special treatment would be illuminating.

When the federal income tax was introduced, in 1913, mineral producers were treated as any other producer, i.e., they were entitled to depreciate the cost of their investment over the expected life of the investment. In 1918 the concept of discovery value depletion was introduced and mineral producers were permitted deductions up to the value of their property. Obviously, this was taken advantage of when the value of the discovery exceeded the cost of acquisition. There is no doubt that when this change was made discovery value depletion was considered to be "a special incentive for exploration and discovery." [10] Difficulties in administering this formula led in 1926 to the

[10] Eugene E. Oakes, "Incentives for Minerals Industries," in *Resources for Freedom* (report of the President's Materials Policy Commission, Washington: U.S. Government Printing Office, 1952), Vol. V. The next two pages draw heavily on this study.

substitution of percentage depletion which permitted oil and gas companies to charge to depletion annually 27½ per cent of gross revenue but not to exceed 50 per cent of net revenue. This advantage was extended in 1932 to metal mines at a rate of 15 per cent, to sulfur at 23 per cent, and to coal at 5 per cent. The privilege was further extended in 1942; and, in the Revenue Act of 1951, a large number of additional minerals were brought in, including sand, gravel, shale, granite, and oyster and clam shells.

It should be noted that the direct impact of percentage depletion is on production rather than discovery. The tax advantage accrues when an income-producing property has been established. But, of course, incentives to discovery are incidentally enhanced by reason of the increased value that percentage depletion bestows on producing properties. The "expensing" of discovery and development costs, on the other hand, constitutes a direct incentive to discovery.

In assessing the character and magnitude of the subsidy three aspects of the concept must be borne in mind. There is no recovery of costs unless an income-producing property is established; there are no cost or value limits to the amount of "recovery," if an income-producing property is established; the extent of the advantage is dependent on the tax obligations of other than mineral producers. If the advantage was moderate when the corporate income tax was 13 per cent, it must be judged to be large with a corporate tax of 52 per cent. In 1948, with the combined corporate normal and surtax rates of 38 per cent in effect, the Treasury figures indicate that percentage depletion was worth $530 millions to the minerals industries.[11] Since then, of course, both the income tax and the earnings of these industries have greatly increased.

There is, of course, a tremendous literature, pro and con, concerning percentage depletion. But I have not been able to discover a satisfactory discussion of what seem to me the two central problems: (1) whether the discovery and replacement of mineral assets presents, for a going concern, an essentially different problem than the acquisition and replacement of manufacturing assets; and (2) if it does, whether

[11] Oakes, *op. cit.,* p. 14. See also Douglas H. Eldridge, "Tax Incentives for Mineral Enterprise," *Journal of Political Economy,* June 1950.

there are any public interest advantages in providing differential tax treatment as against reliance on the price system.

When representatives of the minerals industries talk about the first question they prefer to discuss the trials and tribulations of the "wild-catter" or lone prospector. That there are special risks in mineral discovery and development, at least for the small operator, seems to be clear. If a prospective manufacturer is willing to lay out an adequate sum of money there is little doubt he will be able to build, equip, and staff a producing plant. Whether he will be able to sell the goods is another question. But to all the ordinary business risks of manufacture there are added, for the prospective minerals producer, the risks first, that with a given outlay he will not be in business at all, and second, that if he is in business, with an organization built up at substantial cost and difficulty, he will be able to continue in business when his present ore body or oil field is exhausted.

Although there are many wildcatters and lone prospectors, these discoverers rarely work their own discoveries. The normal practice is to sell out to going concerns. And for mining or oil companies of substantial size, it is difficult to see why the acquisition or replacement of assets presents difficulties any more serious than those of a typical manufacturer. Large companies with geographically dispersed operations are in a position, both in their own discovery activities and through the purchase or lease of discovered properties, to spread—and thus reduce—the risks of acquisition and replacement to somewhere near the levels obtaining in manufacture. And, of course, in the case of producers of sand, gravel, and a number of other minerals, the alleged distinction between mining and manufacture is ludicrous.

Secondly, even if there are special risks, it is doubtful whether there are any public interest advantages in providing differential tax treatment as against reliance on the price system. Many other activities—for example, writing, painting, research and development, and manufacture of fashion goods—face similar risks without special tax treatment. In the absence of tax concessions there are *prima facie* reasons for supposing that price adjustments would, on the average and over time, compensate investors in mining properties at about the same ratio as investors in other properties. And, finally, percentage depletion represents a break in our tax system that has widened with the inclusion of every type of mineral-producing activity regardless of special risk characteristics, and deepened with every rise in the income tax assessed against nonmineral activities.

It is not, however, my purpose here to pronounce a judgment for or against percentage depletion. I wish merely to highlight an important area of inquiry in the political economy of natural resource use. Does the functioning of a competitive price system tend to produce a less than ideal, or socially desirable, investment of resources in mineral discovery and development? If it does, what type of public intervention is best designed to correct this deficiency?

Since I have had occasion to mention the oil industry and will do so frequently later, it is necessary, before proceeding to the next topic, to clear up a possible misapprehension. Our present system of depletion allowances, regulation of output, and import limitation has produced a situation in which there is a very sizable "cushion" between actual and possible production. The availability of this cushion has been considered to be of great importance to the security of the United States. Whether the existence of such a cushion is still important when refining and consuming facilities may be more vulnerable to attack than crude production, is a different question. But it is well to recognize that there is more to the question of an appropriate national oil policy than the merely economic issues that are here under consideration.

The Instability of Raw Materials Industries

The instabilities of commodity markets and their proposed remedies have been so extensively discussed that only a brief recapitulation of the issues need be attempted here.

It is commonly argued that, taking account of supply and demand inelasticities in the raw materials area, an unimpeded functioning of the price system will produce a range of price variation that not only hampers the attainment of ideal investment in natural resource industries, but is much larger than necessary to accomplish "structural" adjustments of production to long-term changes in the pattern of consumption. It is furthermore said that this volatility of raw materials prices, together with fortuitous changes in supply, works great and unnecessary hardship on producers and consumers and, in the case of internationally traded materials, creates foreign exchange difficulties of serious magnitude. To many observers instability of prices and incomes constitutes not only *a* raw materials problem but *the* raw materials problem.[12]

It will be remembered that I am using the word "problem" to mean a set of consequences associated with the working of a free price system that justifies public intervention to bring about what is generally regarded as a better result. Examples of government intervention in the raw materials field are not difficult to find. They tend to fall into two groups: those provoked by real or alleged surpluses with the intervention ordinarily taking the form of supply limitation or government purchase; and those provoked by shortages with, typically, government action in the form of price control or rationing. Even when the real—as distinguished from the putative—purpose of the intervention is stabilization of prices around a trend, the propelling force is ordinarily a producers' or a consumers' group, which raises the question whether the purpose of the intervention is to serve a special or the general interest. But, of this, more later.

The relative instability of raw materials prices as compared with the prices of fabricated products is too well known to require documentation here.[13] The variation in incomes will, of course, depend on quantities as well as prices. And in the minerals industries, where the producers are mainly employed workers, incomes depend primarily on the state of employment. Although some part of observed instability of prices and incomes may be laid at the door of misguided interventionism, there can be no doubt that, in a free price system, the special conditions under which raw materials are produced and

[12] *Cf.,* for example, Myron W. Watkins, "Scarce Raw Materials: An Analysis and a Proposal," *American Economic Review,* June 1944, pp. 239-40. "We may conclude . . . (1) that there is a raw materials problem which in signal respects is different from the general economic problem; (2) that the essence of this raw materials problem is the peculiar susceptibility of these industries to imbalance between supply and demand, both from the short-run and the long-run standpoints; . . ."

[13] See, for example, two United Nations studies: *Instability in Export Markets of Underdeveloped Countries,* 1952, II.A.1; and *Commodity Trade and Economic Development,* 1954, II.B.1.

consumed produce relatively large fluctuations of both prices and incomes.

The term "raw materials," however, covers a wide variety of conditions. About the only relevant characteristic common to all raw materials is that, since they lie far back in the production process, demand is subject to inventory fluctuations, with attendant speculation, at all successive stages. But it is possible to distinguish broad groups of raw materials that tend to exhibit special supply and demand characteristics. Most minerals flow into durable goods industries and consequently reflect, frequently in exaggerated form, the wide cyclical variations in consumption of those industries. On the supply side, reduction of output is usually accompanied by higher maintenance costs than characterize manufacturing operations and cessation of output may be equivalent to loss of the property. Furthermore, expansion of output may, beyond a certain point, be impossible without further discovery.

Many foodstuffs confront demands that tend to be inelastic both to price and income changes. Supply inelasticities are also common in food production either for technical reasons, such as the long growing period of tree crops, or because producers, lacking alternative opportunities, are slow to move in or out of production. The demands for agricultural raw materials are usually more elastic, both price- and income-wise, than for foodstuffs, but supply conditions frequently show the same inelasticities. Beyond these broad generalizations, analysis of price and quantity behavior would find it necessary to proceed to the supply and demand characteristics of particular materials. Still, there are sufficient differences between the production and consumption of raw materials as against manufactures to justify, in large part, the special study of agricultural economics and the less well developed special field of mineral economics.

It does not, of course, follow from these special characteristics and the consequent wide fluctuations of raw material prices that a case has been made for public intervention. But it is equally clear, from observation, that intervention has a peculiar predilection for the field of raw materials and usually on the ground that unimpeded price changes fail to bring about a proper adjustment of supply to demand. To understand and to evaluate this phenomenon takes us out of the field of economics and into that of political economy. The problems really have to do with the nature of the economic setting within which the price and income fluctuations occur and the political-administrative characteristics of the agencies that propose to intervene.

It can be shown, I believe, that, given competitive materials markets and adequate access to a well-developed capital market on the part of people who understand the elementary facts of economic life, producers and consumers can protect themselves from serious difficulties attendant on raw material surpluses or shortages. Even in so-called one-crop countries, elementary precautions with respect to the size of exchange reserves, and public and private behavior permitting access to international capital markets, could permit a substantial stabilization of producers' incomes. Furthermore, the long history of government intervention in this area is not conducive to confidence in the superiority of public action. A recent judgment, with which I largely agree, holds ". . . there is every reason to believe that on balance the effects of government efforts to reduce fluctuations in producers' incomes by operating on prices have been to reduce both output and consumption, and thereby to reduce the world's standard of living." [14]

On the other hand, it does not follow that all intervention to promote stability is in all circumstances misguided. It depends, among other things, on how developed is the capital market, how informed the population, how free from special interest pressures is the government and how effective is the administrative machinery. Given the instability of raw material prices and incomes and the political characteristics of democratic government in both underdeveloped and developed countries, it is clear that stabilization schemes will continue to be attempted. Under these circumstances there is a legitimate task for economic analysis in helping distinguish the better means from the worse. This may be considered by some to be a relatively low type of economic employment. But it remains a fact that the particular char-

[14] P. T. Bauer and F. W. Paish, "The Reduction of Fluctuations in the Incomes of Primary Producers," *Economic Journal,* December 1952, p. 765. This paper was the first in a series of papers and comments on stabilization schemes published in the *Economic Journal,* 1952–54. As a whole, the series constitutes as good a presentation of the economic, political, and administrative issues involved in such schemes as I have seen in the literature.

acteristics of raw materials supply and demand create "problems" that constitute an important part of the political economy of natural resource use.

External Economies and Diseconomies in Natural Resource Use

The concept of external economies entered economics with Alfred Marshall's analysis of decreasing cost industries. An expansion of output in certain industries might bring about economies independent of the action of any firm but accessible to all.[15] The inability of particular firms to secure these economies by their own action supposedly indicated a failure of the "price system" that might be considered to justify government intervention in favor of decreasing cost industries. So defined, external economies have no particular reference to natural resource industries. Nor have they, on examination, revealed themselves to be of any particular importance.

Since Marshall's time the concept has been extended to include a larger class of interdependencies in the economic system; pecuniary interdependencies have been distinguished from technological; and static technological interdependencies have been differentiated from the external economies and diseconomies of economic growth.

A generalized definition of external economies would embrace all economies accruing to a particular firm (or household) by reason of the expansion of output by other firms in the economy and which are independent of their own individual outputs.[16] The expansion of a group of industries, say petro-chemicals and steel, may bring economies to the individual firms in those industries that are impossible to achieve through their own expansion. The expansion of a metropolitan area may bring similar effects. There are likewise economies—and

[15] The Marshallian usage is defined by Viner as follows: "External economies are those which accrue to particular concerns as the result of the expansion of output by their industries as a whole, and which are independent of their own individual outputs." Jacob Viner, "Cost Curves and Supply Curves," *Zeitschrift fur National-ökonomie,* 1931.

[16] *Cf.* an unpublished paper by Svend Laursen prepared for the Center for International Studies at MIT, "External Economies in Economic Development."

diseconomies—contingent on expansion of output in the economy as a whole.

It is important to distinguish between technological and pecuniary economies which, in fact, are not economies at all. In an interdependent system an expansion or contraction of output in any sector is bound to affect prices and incomes in other sectors. These effects involve income transfers that are sometimes called pecuniary economies or diseconomies. But a firm's expansion of output can also affect the physical conditions of production for other firms. An expansion of output in one sector, for example, may create demands for the products of other sectors that permit scale economies to be attained. External consequences affecting outputs that can be obtained from given inputs are true economies (or diseconomies).

It is also important to distinguish static external economies from dynamic. With a given supply of factors of production, expansion of output in one sector will inevitably withdraw inputs from others. Expansion in certain areas may be accompanied by external economies; expansion in others may induce external diseconomies. Since, by definition, these economies are independent of the action of individual firms (or households), if they are large a *prima facie* case is established for public intervention to induce the economies or avoid the diseconomies. The problem posed by static external economies is whether a rearrangement of inputs brought about by some kind of government action will increase total output.

If the assumption of a fixed quantity of factors is abandoned a different aspect of the problem of external economies emerges. The question now is whether in establishing the direction and scale of new investment, important external economies are possible and should be taken into account in making the investment decision. A certain type of investment may contribute to the creation of a trained labor supply that becomes available to other industries and areas. It is also possible that, beyond a certain "critical minimum," large-scale economies appear, outside the area of initial investment, that should be taken into account in determining the level of investment.[17]

There is no reason to believe that if important external economies

[17] The phrase is Harvey Leibenstein's. *Cf.* his *Economic Backwardness and Economic Growth* (New York: John Wiley, 1957).

appear in the process of development, they have any particular affinity for investment in the natural resource area; in fact, the reverse is probably true. But there *is* reason to believe that static external economies and diseconomies are particularly important in the exploitation of natural resources. Almost all the textbook examples of static interdependencies are drawn from this area.[18] An expansion of apple orchards will increase the honey yields of the neighborhood's complement of bees.[19] A cutting of forests on the hillsides may lower the water supply for farm crops in the valley. The exploitation of a river flow for power purposes may neglect gains or losses from flood control, navigation, or other uses. Expansion of oil production from the wells of one owner may increase the real costs and reduce the yields of other owners of the pool. This list could be expanded indefinitely.

Here I am concerned only with a small part of this sizable field of economic analysis relating to external economies. The thesis of this section is, in brief, as follows:

1. That external economies and diseconomies taking the form of static interdependencies are pretty well limited to the natural resource field;

2. That these economies and diseconomies emerge largely because of institutional factors associated with a free enterprise economy and are unlikely to be overcome without government intervention;

3. That, consequently, the examination of external economies and diseconomies and of the means appropriate to the capture of the one and the elimination of the other is a part of the political economy of natural resource use.

There seems to be reason for the concentration of examples of external economies and diseconomies in the natural resource area. These external effects may persist because of lack of knowledge or foresight, or because of institutional or technological obstacles to their capture

---

[18] *Cf.* James E. Meade, "External Economies and Diseconomies," *Economic Journal,* March 1952; Tibor Scitovsky, "Two Concepts of External Economies," *Journal of Political Economy,* April 1954; Svend Laursen, *op. cit.* As Scitovsky puts it (*op. cit.,* p. 145), "The examples of external economies given by Meade are somewhat bucolic in nature, having to do with bees, orchards and woods. This, however, is no accident; it is not easy to find examples from industry."

[19] This is Meade's example, *op. cit.*

or avoidance, or for both reasons. If lack of knowledge is the explanation, there is no particular reason for believing that governmental intervention is the remedy. This observation would appear to be particularly relevant to external economies that may be associated with the process of economic development where lack of foresight may be the critical factor shared in common by private *and* public agencies.[20] On the other hand, the interrelationships may be well known but technological or institutional considerations may prevent their being taken into account. This seems to be particularly relevant in the natural resource area.

Outside the natural resource field, say in manufacturing operations, an awareness of external economies may rather easily lead to appropriate private action. If, for example, in the petro-chemical field an expansion of one process brings economies in the operation of others, combination or integration may bring these economies within the control of management. This happens all the time in manufacture. The legal and economic characteristics of business firms, the organization of the capital market, and the similarity of different manufacturing processes make the capture of many external economies relatively easy.

We may imagine, it is true, a wheat farmer, whose yields are being reduced by forestry operations on surrounding hillsides, taking action by acquiring all the agricultural property in the valley together with the surrounding forested hillsides, and so conducting his joint farming-forestry operations as to take full account of their interdependencies. It is, however, distinctly difficult to do so. The size and organization of the typical agricultural unit, the characteristics of agricultural credit, and the differences in the production and marketing operations involved, all militate against such action. It may be simpler and more effective to handle this and other similar situations that exist within a wide geographical area by public regulation of cutting practices. These regulations may hold private forestry operations somewhat short of the limits to which they would otherwise proceed under the spur of profit maximization, but may also prevent serious diseconomies that private foresters would not ordinarily take into account.

[20] *Cf.* J. A. Stockfisch, "External Economies, Investment and Foresight," *Journal of Political Economy,* October 1955.

The argument for the development of multiple-purpose projects in river valley development is essentially an argument for capturing economies or avoiding diseconomies external to the single purpose that might otherwise be exploited. Government action may be necessary because of the size of the investment or duration of the commitment, or because certain of the advantages—the avoidance of flood damage, for example—may be difficult to bring to charge through the market process.

The unregulated exploitation of oil resources under conditions of multiple ownership of a pool represents a highly important case of external diseconomies. Production from the wells of one owner not only withdraws oil from other owners of land overlying the pool, but may so reduce the gas pressure as to limit the total recovery of all owners. The principal wastes of unregulated oil production are better analyzed under the rubric of external economies than that of conservation as we have defined the term. To be sure, unregulated production may increase current output at the expense of more valuable future output and thus involve a conservation problem, but the principal wastes involve excess inputs per unit of output independently of the timing of production.

The external diseconomies of atomistic oil production are so large that we may hazard the guess that, in the absence of regulation, it would not take a very long time to convince producers of the profit advantages to be obtained by unit operation of oil pools. In other words, it is quite possible that the main wastes of independent production could have been avoided, given time, without regulation so that this is not a legitimate example of a "failure of the price system." Furthermore, regulation, if unavoidable, could have taken the quite different form of compulsory unitization of oil and gas pool operations. But it is obvious that existing methods of regulation are aimed at something more than waste elimination, i.e., at the stabilizing and raising of prices through control of output. Whether unit operation, in addition to eliminating the principal wastes that take the form of external diseconomies, could also serve the interests of conservation, will concern us in the next section.

Even a generalized definition of external economies, tied as it is to the firm as a unit, betrays a certain arbitrariness. If production by the firm embraces a number of processes it is quite possible that expansion of output in one will involve economies or diseconomies for the others. As McKean points out, the Wednesday night sales of a department store may increase the inputs per unit of its daytime sales.[21] But the inclusion of these operations within one "decision-making" unit offers at least the possibility of taking the interdependencies into account. It has been suggested that the recognition of interdependencies among firms is one of the important reasons for combination and integration in manufacture. And it has been emphasized that difficulties of combination and integration in the natural resource field, together with the impossibility under certain circumstances of subjecting economies and diseconomies to market evaluation, may be important reasons why static external economies are peculiarly important in the natural resource area.

But it does not follow, either in manufacture or the natural resource area, that the persistence of external economies or diseconomies necessarily represents a failure of the price system. An attempt to eliminate them by increasing, either through public or private action, the size of the decision-making unit may bring more-than-compensating disadvantages. As we have seen, problems of interdependence exist even within an organization and they tend to increase in complexity, and at a high rate, as the number of distinguishable operations increases. The detection and measurement of such interdependencies is a task for operations research and, as one of the practitioners in this field has remarked, ". . . the best medicine for the well-meaning central planner is, perhaps, a stiff dose of down-to-earth operations research on complex problems of the Federal Government; such an experience would lay bare, more vividly than does meditation alone, the awesome difficulties that would be encountered (and the grim mistakes and the concentration of power that would surely occur) in detailed central direction of the economy." [22]

Operations research, in other words, is no substitute for the price system; nor is indefinite concentration in a single decision-making unit of more or less interdependent economic processes an answer to

[21] Roland N. McKean, "Cost-Benefit Analysis and Efficiency in Government," an unpublished manuscript of RAND Corporation.

[22] McKean, *op. cit.*, p. 9.

the problem of external economies and diseconomies. Some sort of an organizational balance has to be struck with due consideration, on the one hand, of the magnitude of the external economies and diseconomies involved and, on the other, of the administrative—and perhaps political—disadvantages of concentration. It has been suggested that serious unrealized external economies and avoidable external diseconomies are particularly prevalent in the natural resource area. If this is so, analysis of these characteristics, and of possible types of remedial intervention, constitutes an important sector of the political economy of natural resource use.

Conservation

As pointed out earlier in this essay, I propose to limit the meaning of conservation to the elimination or lessening of a particular kind of economic waste: the waste involved in a faulty time distribution of the rate of use of a natural resource. So defined, it is obvious that many issues of traditional interest to conservationists are excluded. But many of these issues—e.g., the wastes in oil production incident to unregulated multiple ownership of a pool—are better discussed under different headings. And other issues—such as the preservation of wildlife sanctuaries or national parks for public use—invoke considerations to which economics has not much to contribute.

If we use the term "conservation" in this admittedly narrow sense, have we defined away all questions of importance in the natural resource field? Are there situations in which the competitive exploitation of natural resources tends to lead to demonstrable wastes in the form of a sacrifice of future public interests to present consumption? If so, are these wastes of sufficient magnitude to establish a *prima facie* case for public intervention?

Despite periodic public alarm at the prospective weakening of the nation's natural resource position (particularly at the time of the Conservation Congress in 1908 and after World Wars I and II), remarkably little public action has been undertaken for the specific purpose of reorienting in time the rate of resource use. Our federal forest land policy and state regulations of cutting and seeding practices probably belong in this category, but it is difficult to find other clear examples. The effect on future yields of overgrazing on public lands was clearly a concern of early conservationists, but the trouble here was not mainly with the price system but with the lack of it. Obviously an unrestricted entry to grazing lands at little or no cost inevitably led to this undesired result. Our oil policy has been primarily concerned with elimination of wastes in the form of external diseconomies, with subsidizing discovery and development, and with price maintenance. Consideration of a "proper" time distribution in the rate of use has played a relatively small role. Even our soil conservation measures, including the current "soil bank," have been mainly directed to the problem of farm surpluses. Practically all our natural resource policies, it is true, have had some effect on the time rate of use, but very few have been designed specifically to accomplish this purpose.

Does this mean that we have been wasting our resources in low-priority consumption at the expense of future generations? If "future" means the next twenty-five to fifty years the answer is quite clearly "no." If, however, we try to push our time horizon much further into the future an attempt to answer this question is bedevilled, on the one hand, by the effect on resource requirements of growth at exponential rates and, on the other hand, the effect on resource availabilities of unforeseen and unforeseeable technological changes. It has been calculated that, if the population of the United States expanded exponentially—that is, on a compound interest basis—at a rate of 3 per cent per annum, a rate which ruled during the period 1790–1860, we should have in this country just four square feet per person by 2314 A.D.[23] According to another calculation, growth of the world's peoples at current rates would produce by 4000 A.D. a population with a total weight equal to the weight of the earth. If now we imagine the consumption of this population growing at the 2 per cent per capita per annum to which we have become accustomed in the United States, total raw material requirements per annum would add up to many times the weight of the earth. Reflection on the effects, over time, of compound interest calculations have led many people to gloomy views indeed. The former director of the Medical Division of The Rockefeller

[23] M. King Hubbert, "Economic Transition and Its Human Consequences," *Advanced Management,* July-September 1941.

Foundation is moved to inquire whether man is a "biological cancer." Mankind has earlier been characterized as a "disease of the dust" and the disease seems to be spreading rapidly. If we take such calculations seriously there is little need to talk about conservation. We might as well consume what we have now since our descendants are going to starve in any case.

There is, however, another school of thought that finds unlimitedly optimistic conclusions in the effects on resource availabilities of continuous advance in science and technology. The de-salting of sea water can cause the deserts to bloom; there are vast untapped mineral resources in low-grade ores and in the sea; and, if this planet gets a trifle congested, the space ships of the future will be available to remove the surplus to other worlds. If this is the preferred vision, it leads equally to the conclusion, but for opposite reasons, that there is little need to worry about the future.

Perhaps because I am merely a pedestrian economist these alternative visions of the future do not greatly stir me. There is really no need to assume that population will increase indefinitely at exponential rates since human institutions and values have shown in the past, and will undoubtedly exhibit in the future, some capacity for adaptation to changing situations. And while science and technology are wonderful, they show no signs as yet of exorcising the persistent fact of scarcity. To undertake a serious discussion of conservation the period of time under consideration has to be limited to that within which one can perceive, at least dimly, the approximate magnitude of the relevant variables.

A consideration of these variables does well to distinguish between conservation applied to particular raw materials and conservation as it relates to broad resource categories such as land and water. Of basic importance to a consideration of particular materials is the high degree of substitutability among both mineral and agricultural products. Agricultural land and, to a less extent, water resources, exhibit, moreover, a great capacity for adaptation to different uses. Our minerals resource base is, of course, much more highly specialized. Although there is large substitutability among groups of mineral products, e.g., ferro alloys, it is difficult to extract copper from an iron ore deposit. The over-all limiting factor to minerals output would appear to be the availability and cost of energy. Given adequate supplies of low-cost energy, minerals from low-grade deposits and from the sea can be conceived as available in nearly unlimited quantities. Thus it is important to draw a distinction between conservation as it affects land, water and, perhaps, energy sources, on the one hand, and conservation as it relates to particular raw material outputs on the other.

Turning to particular materials, it may be useful, for illustrative purposes, to consider the case of lead which appears to be, among minerals, the best candidate for conservation action. On the face of it, the prospects for the future supplies of lead in the United States and in the world look black. The high point for domestic production of primary lead was in 1925 when output totaled 684,000 tons. By 1950 domestic output was down to 430,000 tons. In the meantime the steady increase in United States consumption had reached a figure of 1,423,000 tons by 1950. Despite the rapid expansion of secondary production, the United States has had to import, in recent years, around 40 per cent of total consumption.

The known reserves of lead in this country are very low; not more than three times annual production and not much more than one year's consumption of the primary metal. If inferred reserves are included they amount to perhaps twelve times annual production and six or seven times annual consumption. No discovery of any magnitude has been made in the United States in a generation.

The reserve position in the world as a whole is somewhat better but not by any means easy. In 1950 the President's Materials Policy Commission estimated the world's known and inferred reserves at 27 million tons with world consumption of primary metal running at about 1.6 million tons.[24] Apart from a relatively small find in Greenland, there has not been an important discovery anywhere in the world since the end of the war. The PMPC estimated world requirements for primary lead in 1975 at 2.7 million tons and judged that the prospects for meeting these requirements are "not good." [25]

When we turn to consumption we find that storage batteries and

[24] *Resources for Freedom* (Washington: U.S. Government Printing Office, 1952), Vol. II, Ch. 6. The following discussion of lead is largely drawn from this source.

[25] *Ibid.*, p. 43.

cable coverings account for nearly 50 per cent of domestic use. There appears to be no effective substitute for lead in these uses. Furthermore, the recovery of scrap lead from these uses is exceptionally high: 85 per cent for storage batteries and 90 per cent for cable coverings. On the other hand, there is one use for which recovery is zero. Every year 150,000 tons of lead are blown into the air from the exhaust of gasoline engines and, with the expansion of high-compression engines, this is the most rapidly increasing use. It can hardly be maintained that passenger transport in the United States would be seriously affected by a reduction in the compression ratios for private motor cars. Furthermore, a denial of this use might well lead to the development of substitutes. Are we then, under the guidance of the price system, encouraging low-priority current uses of lead at the expense of future high-priority uses?

Impressive as this case for conservation may appear at first blush, it tends to disintegrate on analysis. The figures on known reserves of lead are of little significance, representing hardly more than working ore inventories, to be expanded when needed. The estimate of inferred reserves are notably inexact. New discoveries will no doubt be made, particularly outside the United States in areas where prospecting, to date, has not been intensive. The flotation process, introduced in the 1920's, made possible the exploitation of lower grade ores and new technological developments may be possible. On the demand side it is worth noting that the former very heavy consumption of lead in paints has almost completely given way to titanium. This suggests that substitution may be possible in other uses. If the PMPC is correct in its assessment of future supplies and requirements, a substantial increase in the real price of lead is indicated which, in itself, can be expected to stimulate the search for supplies and substitutes. Finally, an expectation of even a substantial increase in the real price of a metal is not, in itself, an argument for intervention. If the real price of lead were to double over the next twenty-five years it would require an interest rate of less than 3 per cent to provide an economic justification for curtailment of present in favor of future use. To the best of my knowledge, so rapid an increase in the real price of any material is unknown.

The case for conservation of oil, so heavily pressed in many quarters, is even less convincing. In order to isolate the conservation issue it is necessary to assume that the present regulatory system is abandoned in favor of unit operation of oil pools brought about either by voluntary action or by compulsion. We must further assume that concentration of ownership of pools is not sufficiently great to produce a monopolistic price policy. Under these assumptions the question is this: Would a competitive pricing of oil, with prices equal to the marginal costs of unified pool operations, be expected to lead to a current rate of production and consumption that would sacrifice future high-priority for present low-priority uses? Would oil be used now for, say, oiling roads, at the risk of high real prices or absolute lack of oil for transport ten or twenty years from now? If so, this would presumably represent a failure of the price system justifying intervention in the interests of conservation.

It is, of course, difficult to answer so "iffy" a question with assurance. But the logic of the situation, I submit, runs entirely against such a presumption. As we have seen, unit operation of oil pools can be expected to eliminate the kind of wastes characterized above as external diseconomies. Furthermore, since a large number of separate owners would no longer have to protect their interests against each other by feverish drilling, the spacing of wells would follow a calculation of the economic relation of inputs to expected output. The critical question would appear to be whether competitive pricing would inevitably lead to persistent production in excess of the most efficient rate of recovery, thus lessening substantially the amount of economically recoverable oil at the expense of high—and avoidable—future prices.[26] Is the marginal cost of production so far below the average full cost (including the cost of discovery and development) that marginal-cost-pricing inevitably means sales at less than the cost of replacement? Before concluding that it does, it is well to recognize that marginal costs of operation rise very rapidly in the neighborhood of M.E.R. since production in excess of that rate means a loss of recoverable oil to be charged against current operations. If future

[26] The most efficient rate of recovery (M.E.R.) means a rate that, by sustaining gas pressures, assures the maximum recovery from the pool. (The maximum is obviously an economic rather than a technical limit.)

expected prices are higher than present prices the current costs of operation are obviously enhanced.

I have no doubt that competitive pricing might, on occasion (e.g., with ownerships in weak financial hands and with inadequate access to the capital market) lead to excessive current production. But with unit operation of pools the incentives against such a practice are strong. Competitive determination of output would, of course, produce much greater price variation than exists at present. But, if this is a problem, it is not primarily a conservation problem. Unregulated atomistic production is inevitably wasteful but, here again, these wastes are better analyzed as external diseconomies than as a failure of conservation. If we mean by conservation a proper time distribution of the rate of use, percentage depletion, with its heavy subsidy to current output, is the real danger, not competitive pricing under unit operation of oil pools.

Peering somewhat further into the future, with the whole energy problem of the United States in mind, it is obvious that the price prospects depend substantially on our foreign trade policy. If we treat the United States as a closed economy, the upper limit to a rise in price of natural oil would presumably be set by the cost of oil recovery from shale and coal of which we have large reserves. If we impose no barriers to imports there is no economic reason to expect a rise in oil prices in the foreseeable future. Finally, if account is taken of the potentialities of atomic and, possibly, of solar energy in the not too distant future the question of oil conservation is placed in somewhat clearer perspective.

I have argued, using the examples of lead and oil, that it is difficult to make a case, on conservation grounds, against the output and price results, for particular materials, of an unregulated price system. For particular agricultural products, taking account of the possibilities both of product substitution and of alternative uses of land, the case would appear to be even weaker. When we turn to natural resources in the broad, however, the case may be different. I say *may be* for two main reasons. Our water problems, though serious, do not seem to me to be primarily concerned with conservation in the narrow sense of the term. And it is a little difficult at the present juncture, with wheat and cotton running out of our ears, and with technological improvements increasing agricultural outputs per man and per acre, to take very seriously possible future shortages of food and fibers. Nevertheless when we consider land and water—and possibly energy supplies—as distinct from the particular products of land, water, and energy, we are considering the country's resource base. Any substantial diminution of this base involves a reduction in the potential, not of particular outputs, but of output over-all.

As I have indicated, the major water problems that now confront the United States, though serious, do not seem to me to be, in the main, conservation problems. In the West, where water is scarce, the principal problem seems to be to assure, in the face of numerous claimants, its most productive uses. Among these claimants are politically potent pressure groups and the various states that share control over particular water sources. In part the objective should be to assure the supremacy of the market against the encroachment of special interests. But for those water uses for which the market does not provide an appropriate test, such as recreation and flood control, public intervention is necessary.

East of the Mississippi, a—possibly *the*—major problem is water pollution. Here the primary issue is not conservation—though a comparison of present and future costs and benefits is no doubt involved —but external diseconomies. The discharges of water users upstream, for example, increase the costs per unit of water use downstream. Public intervention may well be needed to purify the discharge or, at least, to assess the cost to its proper source.

The time rate of use, though not the primary issue in the water policies relevant to these problems, nevertheless is a consideration. And it is an important consideration in policies concerned with assuring the continuity of, and moderating the variations in, stream flow. The primary wastes sought to be avoided in multi-purpose river valley development probably belong in the category of external diseconomies; but a close second is waste connected with an improper time distribution of the rate of use.

Public policies relating to agricultural land use exhibit a similar mixture of objectives. But conservation, in the narrow sense of the term, has probably been a more important consideration than in the case of water policy. Our forest land policy has been continuously concerned with the timing of use. The large sum spent on erosion control through education and practical demonstration has been primarily concerned with conservation. While a large part of other public expenditures undertaken in the name of conservation have, in fact, been mainly directed toward the raising of farm income, the preservation of agricultural land for future use has never been lost from sight. And, despite the tremendous increases in productivity per acre brought about by the technological changes of the last few decades, I would maintain that this objective is well chosen. There is little danger, to be sure, that we shall be unable to feed and clothe ourselves, and without significant increases in real costs, for the next twenty-five to fifty years even if we assume a rate of population growth conforming to the maximum census projections. But I would argue that with respect to our land resources we must take the long view. In estimating, for purposes of projection, the relationship between present costs and future benefits in this area the appropriate interest rate may well be close to zero.

Reflection on the distinction between the relevance of conservation considerations to particular materials, on the one hand, and to broad resource categories, on the other, emphasizes the importance of substitution, conditions of replacement, and over-all limitations of supply. Loss of topsoil or source of stream flow is, to say the least, difficult to replace. The serious issues appear to lie in the area of renewable resources and the conservation objective is, by taking appropriate current action, to assure that these renewable resources are, in fact, renewed.

I conclude, then, that although there are many so-called conservation problems that are better considered in other analytical categories, and many assertions of need for conservation that dissolve under scrutiny, there remains a set of conservation issues both real and serious. An analysis of the conditions under which the price system does not assure an effective comparison of present and future costs and benefits, and of various types of public action designed to prevent or rectify these failures, is an important part of the political economy of natural resource use.

Conclusions

This paper has been concerned with four important problems in the political economy of natural resource use. There are, no doubt, others that deserve consideration. But enough has been said, I think, to justify the view that there are special conditions affecting the discovery, production, and consumption of large groups of raw materials meriting the attention of a particular branch of economic analysis. These conditions, affecting the relationships among investment, output, and price in the minerals field, the large variations in price and income that characterize many raw materials industries, the prevalence of external economies and diseconomies, and the relationships between present and future costs and benefits, may or may not produce "failures of the price system" that justify public intervention. But if the questions of "failure" and "justification" are to be considered at all we inevitably move outside the realm of pure economics and into that of political economy.

THE BROADENING BASE
OF RESOURCE POLICY

Robert W. Hartley

Any analysis of what might be called the "political economy of natural resource use" is bound to be controversial. This is true from the outset of Dean Mason's clear and thought-provoking paper. He sets limits on the meaning of the term "conservation" so that it encompasses only the elimination or lessening of a particular kind of economic waste—the waste involved in a faulty time distribution of the rate of use of a natural resource. But if we accept these limits we are led, I believe, to a sympathetic consideration of an important view expressed in the paper—namely, that despite periodic public alarm at the prospective weakening of our natural resources position, remarkably little public action has been taken for the specific purpose of reorienting in time the rate of resource use.

We might well ask the question: Why should this be so? Why should so relatively few of our natural resource policies have been

ROBERT W. HARTLEY, as Vice President and Director of International Studies for The Brookings Institution, is concerned primarily with research and education in international relations. He is a former staff member of the National Resources Planning Board, the Bureau of the Budget, and the Department of State; and was technical adviser to the United States delegation at the United Nations Conference in San Francisco. At Brookings, he collaborated in the surveys on *Major Problems of U.S. Foreign Policy;* edited the periodical, *Current Developments in U.S. Foreign Policy;* and at present is directing a series of studies dealing with the United Nations. Mr. Hartley was born in Dayton, Ohio, in 1911. He obtained his degree from Ohio State University in 1933.

187

designed specifically to affect the time rate of resource use, even though practically all of them have had such effects?

This question can be answered in part by the fact that the development of public policy in the natural resource field has not reached the point where future policy can be based, without a violent and widespread public debate, on the particular kind of economic analysis for which Dean Mason makes such a strong case. The case—as set forth in his paper—seems well proved in the mineral resources field, but it becomes somewhat less convincing when attention is turned to water and land resources, or to the whole field of energy resources. Furthermore, when water, land, and energy resources are taken together, the paper appears to abandon the case and simply declares, ". . . we are considering the country's resource base. Any substantial diminution of this base involves a reduction in the potential, not of particular outputs, but of output over-all."

Here seems to be the key Dean Mason offers for opening the door to the political economy of natural resource use in modern times. If the over-all effect of public policy is to reduce the total resource base, the result is not a desirable one in the national interest. The reasons for this are so obvious that I shall refer to them only briefly.

If we should assume the United States to be a closed economy, a gradual reduction of its total resource base could lead to a weakening of the national economy and eventually its impoverishment, perhaps its complete breakdown. More important, the consequent loss of national power—given the continuation on the international scene of the Soviet-Communist threat—might well imperil our national survival. Even if we do not assume a closed economy, but assume that foreign trade could offset any gradual losses in our resource base, increasing dependence on overseas supplies of raw materials would eventually make us extremely vulnerable to both the cold and hot war tactics of Communist imperialism.

The question I have posed can also be answered in part by the fact that we have had only an imperfect knowledge of the resources that are really available to us and the uses to which they can be put. That knowledge is being rapidly improved, and if the second half of the twentieth century sees as rapid scientific and technological advances as the first half has seen, we may be in the position to develop better natural resource policies.

I will not labor this aspect of the question, because earlier papers in this series have already dealt at length with the subject of science, technology, and natural resources. But I do want to bring out one very important point: as the frontiers of man's knowledge advance and as he is increasingly able to control his environment, his understanding of the natural laws that govern the creation and destruction of matter must inevitably become more profound. Public policies in the resources field will have to be adjusted to that greater understanding, and such adjustment might not be an easy task.

For example, Dean Mason mentions the possibility of the de-salting of sea water, to which I would add the possibility of weather control. If these two possibilities together should be realized, our national policies for water and land resources—if they are to be effective—will have to be formulated within an international framework, because the scope of the problems will have become larger than any one nation's jurisdiction.

I am strongly of the opinion we should start thinking about some of these problems immediately. If the conflict and confusion we have seen over the attempts to achieve international and the national control and exploitation of atomic energy for peaceful uses are any portents of the shape of things to come in other resource fields, then I say we had better get to work now on some of the other advances that are looming ahead.

Finally, I think my first question, about why so little has been attempted toward modifying the rate of resource use, can be answered in part by the fact that in the past, our natural resource policies have been adopted piecemeal. The result frequently has been that their total effect has been one of conflicting objectives and of action at cross purposes.

This brings us to the crucial issue of what the real intent of future public policy should be in the political economy of natural resource use. To limit that intent to conservation alone, as defined in Dean Mason's paper, might not be enough. If the touchstone of future policy is to be only the elimination or lessening of the economic waste involved in a faulty time distribution of the rate of use of a natural resource, then the approach perforce becomes essentially a negative one.

An approach to public policy along these lines inherently means that we are buying time, but for what purpose? In the fields of the nonrenewable resources, we can buy time in order to develop alternative substitutes; in the fields of the renewable resources, we can buy it in order to institute the works and measures that will restore the renewal cycle. Viewed in this light, however, our natural resources policies of the past fifty years could be regarded primarily as stop-gap affairs.

Perhaps we are now at the stage in our national development when we should take a new look at our natural resource policies. This is the obvious and most important conclusion I draw from Dean Mason's paper. It also seems to me that the paper points in the direction of using the over-all approach in such a reappraisal rather than a fragmentary one. Considerations of national security alone would seem to require this way of tackling the problem.

Another conclusion that might be inferred from the paper is that a unified public policy covering water, land, and energy resources might be a highly desirable national objective. I believe the idea of such a unified policy will be increasingly pressed as science and technology open new vistas of the resources that are really available to us on this planet. And if, in the long run, the resources of the earth do not suffice, we might—as Dean Mason guardedly suggests—look elsewhere, for there is little doubt in my mind that we now stand on the threshold of a new age. Whether traditional concepts of the political economy of natural resource use will continue to be valuable to us as we move forward into this new era remains, however, to be seen.

POLICY CRITERIA FOR PETROLEUM

✍ *Minor S. Jameson, Jr.*

Dean Mason has referred several times to special interests and quite a few times to oil. I represent both, as part of what is referred to in some circles as "the oil lobby." This kind of activity is an important element in our form of government, under which the different groups have an obligation to present their viewpoints and the relevant facts so that informed public decisions can be made.

Dean Mason points out that land and water—and possibly energy supplies—are the country's resource base, any substantial diminution of which would involve a reduction in the potential, not of particular outputs, but of output over-all. I would include energy without the qualification of "possibly." The importance of petroleum (oil and natural gas) as a part of that resource base is shown by the fact that oil and natural gas now furnish more than twice the total amount of energy supplied by other mineral fuels and water. In the area of public

---

MINOR S. JAMESON, JR., Executive Vice President of the Independent Petroleum Association, has been connected with that association for the past twenty years. He is a member of the Military Petroleum Advisory Board. At the time of the Korean War, and again during the Suez crisis, he acted as consultant on petroleum to the Department of the Interior; and in connection with the Cabinet Committee on Energy Supplies and Resource Policy he has been consultant to the Office of Defense Mobilization. Mr. Jameson was born in Worcester, Massachusetts, in 1911. He received his degree in business and engineering administration from the Massachusetts Institute of Technology in 1934.

191

policy, therefore, oil and natural gas present problems of particular importance.

One authority on resources and conservation, Professor Erich W. Zimmermann,[1] points out that in the popular conception of resources no distinction is made between physical substances and resources. He describes physical substances as the "neutral stuff" of nature that does not become a resource until man (*a*) becomes aware of the substance, (*b*) learns how to make use of it, and (*c*) develops ways of making the substance available for use. This concept has vital implications, in his judgment, for the meaning of resource conservation in general and petroleum in particular. In the case of oil the distinction between the physical substance and the resource is of vital significance. The oil industry lives on the process of discovering and developing additional reserves to replace the oil that is being consumed. Professor Zimmermann concludes that if resources "are not but become," if they unfold slowly in response to evolving wants and arts, then the first concern of those who would do something for posterity should be to make sure that this unfolding process proceeds unhindered.

It seems to me that this unfolding process—the conversion of nature's "neutral stuff" into resources—bears directly on what Dean Mason terms a central question of natural resource economics here at issue, namely: Are the conditions of mineral discovery and production so different from other types of production as to require special analysis and special treatment? He questions whether oil should be treated differently, through tax policy, state conservation laws, or foreign trade policies. I believe that petroleum has unique characteristics, affecting discovery, development, and production, that justify differential treatment in certain areas of public policy. The economic progress and security of this country are closely related to our energy supplies in general and our petroleum supplies in particular. The question goes beyond actual war; in a nuclear war we might have little or no use for whatever supplies we had. The real problem relates to such incidents as the closing of the Suez Canal. In that instance no one knows what would have happened if Europe had not been able to draw upon the

[1] Erich W. Zimmermann, *Conservation in the Production of Petroleum* (New Haven: Yale University Press, 1957).

Western Hemisphere for vital supplies of petroleum. I agree, however, that a lack of satisfactory information on the special position of petroleum has been, and continues to be, a deterrent to definitive analysis. The development of more adequate information, necessary for any meaningful economic evaluation, relating to the discovery and development of petroleum resources may be one of the major problems in the subject under consideration here.

Much information is available, of course, on petroleum resources, their development and use. Yet the deficiencies are serious in the fund of knowledge and the degree of effort in the field of petroleum economics. I doubt that any equally significant area of public policy has been subject to as much attention with as little appreciation of the complex of technological, economic, and political factors involved. Economic research has lagged far behind advances in technology. The petroleum industry probably can claim the dubious distinction of providing more basic goods, with less understanding of its economic processes, than any other industry.

There is a real need for more information and more objective research on risk factors in establishing capital values in the form of petroleum resources, where more than $5 billion each year is expended in the unfolding process of maintaining the country's energy resource base through discovery and development of additional petroleum reserves. Certainly, there may be many occupations as risky as petroleum exploration. But I question if there are any involving as large recurring expenditures of capital with as important an influence on the national economy.

Even if complete information were available, I would find it difficult to consider the problems of natural resources within any limited definitions of conservation, or to isolate the economic issues. In the case of petroleum, the geologist seeks to broaden the horizon for potential producing provinces; the engineer seeks to advance the technology of recovering oil and gas from their underground reservoirs; the lawyer is concerned with correlative rights and jurisdictional questions; the economist is concerned with possible maldistribution of capital in petroleum development through differential treatment; the military is concerned with a mobilization base of adequate oil for emergencies; while public officials formulate and administer petroleum policies within a maze of national and international considerations. As Dean Mason points out, there is more to the question of appropriate national oil policies than the merely economic issues. Solutions to problems in the area of public policy as to petroleum resources necessarily are reduced to judgments as to the best practical courses of action.

Under the public policies as to differential tax treatment for petroleum and state regulation of production that have obtained over the past quarter of a century, oil and natural gas have supplied a steadily increasing share of the energy base for the country's expanding economy. Evidence over a long period as to the *net* result, in terms of over-all economic progress as well as national security, is impressive in support of petroleum policy judgments that have been made. Under these policies an adequate, continuous supply of petroleum has been provided at prices that enabled the growth in oil and gas use at a faster rate than the expansion in the general economy. This in no sense overlooks the problems under consideration here. On the contrary, petroleum policies are of increasing and particular concern.

Today, for example, federal regulation of natural gas production and national policies as to oil imports are immediate issues with far-reaching implications. Proper solutions to such problems cannot be found within the independent concepts of law, technology, economics, or security planning. The appropriate course of action inevitably involves conflicting viewpoints and compromise.

If utility-type price controls of natural gas prices at the well impair the development of this energy resource, as would be expected, is there a net gain or loss to the total economy? If increasing imports mean temporarily lower prices and encouragement of foreign trade, but also vulnerability to loss of supplies, such as resulted from the closing of the Suez Canal, and to the demands of other nations, which is the better course of action? Clearly, such questions go beyond the interests of the parties directly concerned—importing companies and domestic producers, for example. These are areas of public policy, as recognized in the appointment of a Cabinet-level committee to study the oil import problem. The following conclusion by that committee in its July 1957 report serves to illustrate that the issues are not limited to economic considerations:

Domestic consumers are utilizing an increasing amount of petroleum products for transportation, fuel, heating and many other aspects of consumer life. In the event of a national emergency, it is essential to these consumers that there be adequate supplics at reasonable cost, both now and in the future. The low cost of imported oil is attractive, but excessive reliance upon it in the short run may put the nation in a long-term vulnerable position. Imported supplies could be cut off in an emergency and might well be diminished by events beyond our control. This vulnerability could easily result in a much higher cost, or even in the unavailability, of oil to consumers. It is therefore believed that the best interests of domestic consumers, as well as of national security, will be served if a reasonable balance is maintained between domestic and foreign supplies.

In conclusion, I want to re-emphasize what appears to me to be a basic problem in the field of natural resource policy, particularly as to petroleum exploration and development. This is the lack of adequate information and adequate economic research, resulting in widespread misunderstanding as to the unfolding process of converting nature's "neutral stuff" into oil and gas resources. If petroleum supplies are important to our energy base for both economic progress and security, it becomes important that changes in public policy be based on conclusive evidence that gains from such changes unquestionably more than offset probable losses. This should be the overriding criterion in any study of natural resource problems and policies.

NOTE BY MR. MASON   I agree with Mr. Jameson on the importance of an oil cushion for security interests. It is a tremendous thing for the West that at the time of the Suez crisis we had a sizable cushion in the United States.

There is no doubt that the percentage depletion and the system we have in this country makes for a sizable cushion. In my paper I refrained from discussing the security aspects of the oil industry. I was giving an economist's view of the problem—whether in economic terms you could justify government intervention subsidizing oil discovery and development. Obviously, all kinds of political considerations intervene in the determination of policy with respect to natural resource use, all kinds of political considerations that I did not attempt to take account of.

THE WANING ROLE OF LAISSEZ FAIRE

✍ Bushrod W. Allin

Professor Mason begins his paper with a discussion of the meaning of conservation, and ends it with the conclusion "that there are special conditions affecting the discovery, production, and consumption of large groups of raw materials . . . that *may or may not* [underscoring mine] produce 'failures of the price system' that justify public intervention." He then says ". . . if the questions of 'failure' and 'justification' are to be considered at all we inevitably move outside the realm of pure economics and into that of political economy."

But the title of his paper indicates that he is discussing problems in political economy—not problems in pure economics. Actually, his purpose seems to be only to highlight important areas of inquiry into the political economy problems of natural resource use. And I think he has done an excellent job of this.

Economics, to him, appears to mean the "unfettered price system," and political economy includes government intervention. Using this

---

BUSHROD W. ALLIN is an agricultural economist, who has been with the United States Department of Agriculture since 1921. In 1934–35 he assisted in a nationwide study of population redistribution with the Wharton School of Finance, University of Pennsylvania. He is a member of the American Farm Economic Association and American Economic Association. He is the co-author of *Migration and Economic Opportunity,* and the author of many bulletins and articles in the Department of Agriculture and Land Grant College publications. He was born in Harrodsburg, Kentucky, in 1899, and received his Ph.D. from the University of Wisconsin in 1927.

differentiation, he highlights *problems* of political economy through-out his paper when he repeatedly raises a question in connection with current "extensive" government intervention in natural resource use. That question is: "Whether intervention has been, or is, justified in the public interest, or whether it represents merely the pressure of special interests." I suspect he is right in most of the places where he more than gently hints that activities carried on in the name of "con-servation" may be serving a special interest more liberally than the public interest. But how are we to deal with this problem? This type of problem is, as he clearly implies, a problem in political economy—not pure economics.

Obviously, no one essay can cover all the implications of this ques-tion as they relate to even a few of the situations pointed out by Pro-fessor Mason—to say nothing of providing the answers. By way of supplementing his paper, let me direct attention to the problem area he defines as conservation. He says that "if conservation is defined as the avoidance of waste in natural resource use," a discussion of all four of his categories of problems of political economy is relevant to a discussion of conservation. But he prefers to restrict the meaning of conservation to "the avoidance of wastes associated with a faulty time distribution of the use of resources."

I see no reason why he should not use his own definition, except perhaps to point out that a Gifford Pinchot, a Theodore Roosevelt, or a Hugh Bennett wouldn't recognize an external economy or disecon-omy if he met one coming down the road in broad daylight.

If I interpret his paper correctly, he believes that the unfettered price system has not served well the conservation of our soil, water, and forest resources—and that some government intervention is de-sirable. This is true especially in the case of soil, where he says "the long view" is necessary— and that "in this area the appropriate inter-est rate may well be close to zero." I agree. But having arrived at this judgment (and I suspect not by way of economic analysis but by ob-servation and experience), he has just begun to discuss the political economy problems of land use in the interest of conservation. He has said that they lie outside of pure economics. But what kinds of gov-ernment intervention are desirable and workable?

Consider, for example, the Dust Bowl. Everybody agrees that much of the land in that area should be returned to grass and kept there. But an important roadblock to this goal is private property rights in land—an economic institution that has become a sturdy feature of our culture. How does the public in this circumstance achieve a control of land use in the public interest and at the same time serve the special interests of existing owners? We have several operating public programs, the latest of which is under Public Law 1021, in which the government enters into contracts with landowners for specified periods of time. All of the existing programs rest on the assumption that demonstration, education, and public assistance will do the job. None of them is recognized as intervention or interference, except in the case of the rare exercise of the police power by a soil conservation district as a local unit of government. Thus, the tradition of permitting the individual landowner to do as he pleases is itself an obstacle to needed government intervention.

Problems in political economy have a way of becoming blurred as to purpose—often intentionally. They defy all efforts at classification into mutually exclusive compartments. Narrow definitions are helpful for what Professor Mason calls "rational analysis"; but for social and political judgments and for social inventions to deal with problems in political economy the broader definitions can be useful at times without being irrational. Witness, for example, the evolution of soil conservation and other agricultural legislation. There is not the slightest question that the purpose to raise farm income reinforced the purpose to promote soil conservation, and vice versa. The interrelation between soil conservation and national programs for dealing with the problems of farm surpluses and farm incomes is quite clear in the historical process by which we have made great strides during the last quarter-century in soil conservation. Indeed, there must often be such interrelationships in the actions of democratic government, for the action of such government is usually a process of compromising conflicting interests and integrating multiple purposes. To the extent that government subsidies become greater than appear reasonable for conservation purposes, they are often judged by some to be serving other purposes. At that point they are presumably no longer payments for conservation under Professor Mason's definition of conservation, but are subsidies for something else. And the something else may or may not be merely a special interest.

When Adam Smith first advocated his "unfettered" price system, he was trying to make government serve the public interest rather than merely the special interests of the kings, nobles, and privileged classes. But too many of his disciples have believed that "laissez faire" was itself *the* method for finding out what the public interest is. They conceive of the government as primarily a police force for enforcing laissez faire. The truth is, of course, that the government at any given time is whatever interests are in control of it; and the *it* they are in control of is the power to make their interests prevail. The more nearly the interests of those in control of government approach those of the public generally, the more nearly government itself approaches the ideal. But the logic of pure economics under laissez faire is only one of the useful tools for discovering and agreeing upon what the public interest is. Others include an understanding of institutions such as those relating to land tenure, governmental forms, and public administration.

A favorite technique by which special interests that are not also public interests thwart the will of our legislators, even when they have passed a bill having a public purpose, is to stack the administrative arms of government with personnel whose purpose is only to serve a special interest. This procedure is regularly creating a whole collection of political economy problems. Professor Mason is aware of all of this. I only wish he had included it in his paper, along with the suggestion that one of the real functions of the regulatory and administrative arms of government is that of investigation to help the conflicting interests find the public interest. When they find it, it must be one that is workable—not Utopian.

In his discussion of "the instability of raw materials industries," Professor Mason agrees with "a recent judgment" that "there is every reason to believe that on balance the effects of government efforts to reduce fluctuations in producers' incomes by operating on prices have been to reduce both output and consumption, and thereby to reduce the world's standard of living." But he then goes on to say, "it does not follow that all intervention to promote stability is in all circumstances misguided." Those of us who have been trying to do this for

American agriculture wish to commend him for this last statement. At another point he says that "it is clear that stabilization schemes will continue to be attempted." I would add that even if all past efforts had failed, that fact alone would be no reason to stop trying.

Since attempts at stabilization will continue, he suggests that there is a "legitimate task for economic analysis in helping distinguish the better means from the worse." But then he adds (while reserving his own opinion): "This may be considered by some to be a relatively low type of economic employment." I have been associated for thirty years with people engaged in this employment. Sometimes we, too, venture some judgments on the value of different kinds of economic work and our kind does not come out at the bottom of the scale.

Aside from all this, Professor Mason has written a thoughtful paper that should be helpful to all students of natural resource use. Its breadth of scope is a testimonial to his scholarship and great analytical powers. What I think he has done, essentially, is to point up the limitations of laissez faire economics in dealing with the political economy problems of natural resource use. One of these limitations is our cultural affinity for laissez faire doctrine, especially on the part of those who have special-interest axes to grind that not only are not public interests but are also often in direct conflict with the public interest as it would be defined by any representative group of interests.

Perhaps a part of the significance of his paper is to be found in the fact that a nationally known Harvard political economist considered it fruitful to discuss in the year 1958 the central question he poses. Too much of our economics tends to glorify individual action to the virtual exclusion of all else; while collective action and the working rules of collective action are the dominant facts of modern economic life everywhere. Political economy finds a place for, and studies, both kinds of action. And that includes the action of the makers of both economic and political "demand," who too often mean by the unfettered price system only the absence of public fetters in the public interest.

NOTE BY MR. MASON   Mr. Allin has raised some interesting questions concerning the role of a government economist. An economist, if he is properly trained and is sensible, has a technique of analysis that can make a contribution to a problem, if he sticks to his techniques and leaves it to the politicians and others to make their guesses as to what the strength of various interest groups is going to be.

But I would hate to see government economists spending any more attention than they do now to second-guessing politicians on how Congress is going to behave with respect to particular measures.

I defined conservation as narrowly as I did because I believe that economists can make their largest contribution to an examination of natural resource problems if they distinguish fairly sharply between fundamental issues and those that are not so important.

VI 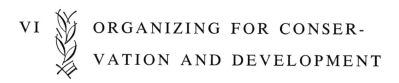 ORGANIZING FOR CONSERVATION AND DEVELOPMENT

BROADER BASES FOR CHOICE:
THE NEXT KEY MOVE

✍ Gilbert F. White

Wherever resources conservation and development is discussed the final and sometimes interminable topic is who should do what—what organizations should be devised or strengthened to help us achieve our aims in resources development. In this final paper of the series, my contribution cannot be that of one deep in administration of resources activities or who delves into the political mysteries; it is, rather, that of a person who is trying to see and understand the impression of human organization upon the American landscape of rock, soil, water, vegetation, and people.

The aims of the American people concerning that landscape have

---

GILBERT F. WHITE is Chairman of the Department of Geography at the University of Chicago. His career has to a rare degree combined scholarly with administrative and service activities, particularly in the field of water resources. For the ten years prior to 1956 he was President of Haverford College. During and preceding this period he was directly concerned with water resources, first in the 1930's with the National Resources Board and the National Resources Planning Board, and later with the Bureau of the Budget. The war years saw him in France administering relief for the American Friends Service Committee, of which he was appointed assistant executive secretary. In 1948, while President of Haverford, he served as a member of the committee on natural resources of the Hoover Commission, and again in 1950 served as Vice Chairman of the President's Water Resources Policy Commission. Lately, during 1956–57, he was Chairman of the United Nations Panel on Integrated River Basin Development. Besides numerous government reports, Mr. White is the author of *Human Adjustment to Floods*. He was born in Chicago in 1911, and received his Ph.D. at the University of Chicago in 1942.

changed more in variety than in species since the conservation movement took root fifty years ago. The methods for carrying out those aims have involved a multiplication in numbers of organizations but relatively few fundamental innovations in form. The tools for assessing the success or failure of these ventures, while still far from adequate, are much improved. We know enough, at least, to ask a few basic questions and perhaps to suggest some of the answers.

Why have states generally failed to exercise a strong hand in most resources fields other than wildlife management? Why have attempts to consolidate the splintered federal agencies been prevented? Why has formal co-ordination of federal and federal-state agencies usually been meager in returns except in forest management? Why has "partnership" between federal and private enterprise been largely fictional and often exploitive? Why have articulate, aggressive interest groups played an increasingly powerful role? The reasons are many and complex. I shall examine only a few of them. As for positive suggestions, I must warn in advance that I shall conclude by stressing a line of action that in recent years has been considered old hat—no more modern, perhaps, than the idea of a daily period of family meditation, but perhaps as needed in a confused and harassed society. And even if accepted, my suggestion would promise no early end to agency rivalries and program conflicts.

I am not unaware of the more thoroughgoing and ambitious solutions that have been proposed. It may be useful here to outline the range of remedies that are offered from time to time. I list them not by way of endorsement—some of them appeared more promising to me ten years ago than they do today—but to indicate the diversity of views which some others have of the problems at issue.

What was recognized as a general need in 1908—to provide integrated management of resources over entire units of area—appears to be among the urgently felt needs in 1958. This may be illustrated with one resources field that has been trampled by more earnest survey parties than any other—the nation's water resources. The administration of water resources now involves division of authority among eight major and numerous minor federal agencies. Many of these are single purpose; others are in conflict over multiple-purpose programs. Each state has several agencies in the field; few have unified administration, only a half-dozen at most have genuinely strong organizations capable of planning and carrying out sizable works.[1] Given the widely accepted ideal of integrated development of multiple-purpose projects for entire basins for the public good, the present arrangement seems unduly wasteful and ineffective. Five public commissions in nine years have looked into aspects of the situation and have prescribed remedies.

The suggestions for organization run as follows: [2]

1. Consolidate and regroup the agencies to reduce duplication and competition and to facilitate co-operation among agencies performing related activities.

2. Unify the basic policies so that, regardless of organization, there will be harmonious means of judging projects, assessing repayments, and co-operating with local groups.

3. Reallocate resources functions among Congressional committees with a view to promoting unified definition of policies and of agency procedures.

4. Establish a national review agency, either as an independent board or as a branch of the Bureau of the Budget, to provide impartial review and to define the policy issues involved in new project proposals.

5. Set up some kind of co-ordinating mechanism—a co-ordinator in the President's office, a co-ordinating committee of agencies, or regional co-ordinating committees including state representatives—to reconcile the plans and actions of the different agencies.

6. Carry out a vigorous program of public information in order to build understanding of the issues involved so that when a crisis or some great enlightenment as to a constructive aim favors action, it will be in the direction of sweeping improvements.

7. Promote greater participation by state and local agencies and private groups in planning, constructing, and operating the needed works.

[1] Council of State Governments, *State Administration of Water Resources* (Chicago, 1957).

[2] A number of the policy issues are reviewed by Fesler and, in another framework, by Irving K. Fox, "National Water Resources Policy Issues," *Law and Contemporary Problems,* XXII (1957), 472-509.

Other answers have been put forward from time to time. For example, the valley authority alternative still finds favor in some quarters. These will suffice to indicate the sorts of remedies that are on the table and, indirectly, the ailments in the body politic which they are intended to heal.

They have been discussed long and often, and little has been done about them. An impressive series of arguments may be marshalled for and against each proposed reform. The arguments against often have a circular pattern, as for example: it would do little good to consolidate agencies because the basic policies are in conflict; a unified water policy cannot be enacted because of divisions among Congressional factions and committees; Congressional committees cannot be reformed because the executive activities are divided among several departments each with its own cluster of supporting interest groups; public information is handicapped by the existence of separate agencies promoting under Congressional direction their own separate programs.

Somewhat similar arguments may be raised with respect to organization in other fields such as public lands and energy production. In themselves they do not seem a sufficient reason for lack of progress during the last fifty years.

The entrenchment of agencies and their associated interest groups and Congressional connections often is advanced as a principal reason for resistance to any substantial change in organization. Lines and sinews of bureaucratic empires undoubtedly play a role, but I don't believe they are the answer, either. It seems likely from the record that deeper conflicts and uncertainties as to social aims and means play a larger role. These now will be reviewed, first the aims, then the means.

While there have been shifts of emphasis among the basic aims of government agencies involved in the management of natural resources, there has been relatively little change in the broadly stated objectives during the fifty years since the Inland Waterways Commission and the Governors' Conference stated so many of them. Ernest Griffith in the first essay of this series has noted some of the persistent strands in these activities; they also have been described by Dana and Engelbert.[3]

When the various declarations of aim in our management of resources over the past fifty years are charted according to time and character there is much similarity among the fields of soil, water, forests, and minerals. Our stated aims are vague and have remained at about the same level. In all instances the federal government, while generally solicitous to prevent destruction of publicly owned lands and forests, has not sought to regulate or penalize destruction by private landowners. Very similar kinds of measures have been enacted with respect to research, information, development measures in a number of the resource fields, but we have seen little in the direction of regulation of the use of resources by private managers.

Once the nation moved out of the period in which resources were being distributed from the public to private hands into a period of stewardship of the remaining public resources, we find that regulation is employed by the federal government, and to a large extent by the state governments, chiefly to prevent injury to other property holders, as, for example, to keep the owner of a forest from injuring a nearby owner by letting fire go unimpeded; or to prevent the spread of plant diseases, or the destruction of migratory waterfowl, or the wasteful drawing down of an oil pool.

The nature of the public interest in what private owners do still is unclear. It is still possible for a farmer to gully and gut a farm at his own pleasure without public restraint. It is still possible for a timber owner in most states of the Union to wantonly destroy forests if he wishes. It is still possible for a coal operator to take only 5 per cent of a vein out of the ground and leave the rest there, perhaps irretrievably so. Some restraints are exercised, but by and large the public expression of a definite judgment of what constitutes waste or what constitutes wise use or what constitutes wise development has changed very little since 1908.

[3] Samuel T. Dana, *Forest and Range Policy: Its Development in the United States* (New York: McGraw-Hill, 1956); Ernest A. Engelbert, *American Policy for Natural Resources: a Historical Survey to 1862* (Harvard University, unpublished dissertation, 1950).

Two trends, however, are discernible. With respect to stewardship, there has been a shift from emphasis upon preservation to emphasis upon development, from saving resources to maximizing the benefits from their use, although it is unlikely that the full panoply of development techniques practiced today in a national forest reserve or a western drainage basin would go far beyond the expectations of Pinchot and Powell before the turn of the century. We now look to the federal government for investment and administration as well as scientific and research services. This increasing stress on positive development was one major trend in aim.

Direct federal subsidy or tax incentive has been used chiefly to influence private operators either to encourage and strengthen development efforts, as in the case of irrigation and much watershed protection, or to stabilize their incomes, as in the case of depletion allowances for mineral discovery, with resource preservation or wise use being a secondary objective. Agricultural conservation payments, for example, were not primarily intended to save the soil.

A second major trend was the shift from single-purpose to multiple-purpose aims. Multiple-purpose concepts were not lacking in public discussions and reports in 1908, but they found their way into concrete state and federal legislation slowly. The number of resource uses for which some public action seemed warranted multiplied, and with them the avowal, more often in preambles and speeches than in action programs, of a belief in multiple-use management. Along with this there has been a constant struggle to somehow combine the idea of achieving scale economies and other economies with the ecologist's concept of equilibrium in the web of nature, a kind of reconciliation that we haven't fully achieved in theory let alone in practice.

It is difficult to overestimate the impelling sense of community with nature which has shown itself, not only dramatically in the desire to preserve places of primeval beauty, but persistently in efforts to prevent the unbalanced destruction of segments of the "seamless web." Here, as in other branches of human endeavor, it is constructive striving toward harmonious life and knowledge, rather than defensive action against threatening disaster, that often claimed imaginative intelligence.

What about the agencies that the American people have maintained or created to carry out this set of aims? The chief trend in organization during the fifty years has been to establish or strengthen single-purpose agencies. This is not surprising in view of the application of loosely defined objectives to more and more fields and the shift of emphasis toward positive development for multiple purposes. As the need was felt for more vigorous action in particular fields such as hydroelectric power, soil conservation, national parks, or water-pollution abatement, new units were set up, for the most part in the departmental structure, and a kind of splintering operation went on. This appears to have been as true at the state level as at the federal level.

Most of the new or enlarged agencies followed traditional patterns of bureau organization, but a few were innovations, and as such they deserve attention. One was the Federal Power Commission, which among other duties was given responsibility for weighing proposed licenses in the light of comprehensive schemes for improvement for navigation, power, and other beneficial public uses. But in terms of the purposes contemplated by the old Inland Waterways Commission, the FPC has never reached its goal. It did not exercise that development function in a positive way, and left the planning initiative largely to prospective licencees or to other public agencies.

A second innovation was the interstate compact mechanism, used not only as a means of establishing boundaries and water rights but also of promoting further allocations and uses of resources. It may be too early to assess some of those experiments which, like the Potomac and Upper Mississippi River water-pollution agreements, have operated only a few years. But assessment of others is needed and is in progress. Some of the more impressive records of development, affecting fisheries, water pollution, and oil, have been linked with regulatory powers. However, the Interstate Oil Compact Commission regulated oil production primarily to prevent surfeit and price deterioration, with the "conservation" effects being less certain. The enthusiasm for new interstate mechanisms has waned somewhat in recent years as the earlier ventures such as the Colorado and Rio Grande commissions have run into long delays. Probably none of the uses of this device in the resources area has had the success of the interstate ventures in parole systems, regional education, and metropolitan transport development.

Another innovation is the use of international treaties and commissions in resource problem areas. Some encouragement may be drawn from this experience. Performance under the migratory waterfowl and seal fishing treaties has been substantial; and the joint water commissions on the Canadian and Mexican borders, notwithstanding the lack of a comprehensive program for the Columbia, enjoy the distinction of being the most productive of concrete action of any in the world picture. At times the United States seems to have dealt more effectively with the resources problems when it collaborated with its neighbors than when it had the problem all to itself at home.

Upon the earlier experience of irrigation, drainage, and levee districts, soil and water conservation districts have been expanded at a rate great enough to be considered an innovation. The Miami Conservancy District pattern was modified in a few other areas for water development, and state laws made possible the organization of county or other local soil conservation districts in large numbers. Neither type of district has achieved the hoped-for decentralization of planning and operation responsibility. The larger water-regulation districts were hamstrung by the federal policy, initiated in 1937, of paying 100 per cent of the cost of flood-control reservoirs. The Muskingum district is an example. The soil conservation districts have tended to become political supports for the planning and technical activities of personnel of the Soil Conservation Service and do not bear heavy responsibility as districts for either initiating or carrying out farm plans; neither are they effective instruments for carrying a national land-use policy to those areas. Here, too, the tendency has been to splinter into agencies serving relatively limited purposes.

Two other innovations sought to integrate resource development activities at a subnational level; they were the state planning boards and the Tennessee Valley Authority. The planning boards flourished for a time under the encouragement of public works planning and the National Resources Planning Board, but with a few exceptions after 1944 they either died out or were converted into industrial promotion or capital budgeting agencies. There were complex reasons, which I cannot fully assess, for their rise and fall. Some no doubt lacked viability of function or organization; some were independent appendages, fully exposed to the whole swing in public opinion against government intervention; but a major reason must have been the absence of a national agency with which to collaborate, after the National Resources Planning Board was abolished under the pressure of federal agencies and Congressional blocs.

If concrete accomplishment in transforming the water and energy regimen of an area is the criterion, the TVA was the one clearly successful innovation. More in other parts of the world than in the United States it is the outstanding example of application of human effort and ingenuity to developing the water and land resources of the area. Why then does it stand alone in the United States? And why has every other country which has tried a similar regional authority ended with only one example? The difficulties and advantages of expanding the valley authority have been examined thoughtfully by McKinley.[4] For the reasons he states, especially the difficulty of reconciling a wholly regional orientation with national needs and with the work of national agencies, creation of additional valley authorities seems both unwise and impracticable. Nevertheless, I believe today, as I did ten years ago, that unless basic improvements are made in both policy and organization in the water field, the valley authorities might be preferable to the prevailing arrangements. In this respect a particularly important asset of the TVA (so long as it is permitted to discharge its appointed functions) is its competitive influence upon the standards and practices of the national water agencies.

To sum up, few of our innovations in resources organization are strikingly fresh and new; and none seems to hold promise for improvements on the large scale that is needed and desired.

In our present state of knowledge so sweeping a generality must, of course, be highly tentative. Not all the evidence is in, and not all of the data that are available have been satisfactorily analyzed. We still have a rather clumsy set of instruments with which to measure the full impact of organized efforts to conserve and develop resources. No innovation, for example, has been described more fully or debated more hotly than the Tennessee Valley Authority. It was established as

[4] Charles McKinley, *Uncle Sam in the Pacific Northwest* (Berkeley: University of California Press, 1952), pp. 567-635.

an experimental and demonstration area. Its physical works and its social programs are well known, yet its net effect upon both the natural and the human resources of its region are difficult to appraise. How much of the change in level of living stemmed from forces which would have been at work in any event both in the region and in the entire southeastern section? Was its soil conservation program more effective in saving soil and building stable homes than the competing Soil Conservation Service program? Did the organization indeed operate at the grass roots in making major decisions? Did it place national interest above local interest? There are rough means of approaching these and other problems. For example, it now appears that the TVA arrived at its more crucial decisions with the local interest uppermost but without grass roots participation.[5] But on many other points we must rely upon strictly curbstone opinions.

Until the recent work of Krutilla and Eckstein,[6] and by some of the Harvard group, there have been few even slightly refined means of judging the net impacts upon regional and national economy of alternative programs of water regulation for hydroelectric power and navigation. Thus, a balanced comparison of the probable social results from the Hells Canyon project under federal versus private management was lacking during the time when political controversy over those rival plans was most intense.

One of the principal arguments for new irrigation enterprises in the West is their stabilizing effect upon surrounding dry-land agriculture, yet we have only begun to establish the true effects. A recent study of the Uncompaghre project in Colorado indicates that, as a result of division of responsibility among three different agencies, the net result probably was to disrupt rather than stabilize the grazing economy.[7] Experience of the Bowaters Southern Paper Corporation in East Tennessee suggests that promotion and investment in a new wood-proces-

[5] R. G. Tugwell and E. C. Banfield, "Grass Roots Democracy: Myth or Reality?", *Public Administration Review,* 10, pp. 47-55.

[6] John V. Krutilla and Otto Eckstein, *Multiple Purpose River Development* (Baltimore: The Johns Hopkins Press, 1958); and Otto Eckstein, *Water Resources Development: The Economics of Project Evaluation* (Cambridge: Harvard University Press, 1958).

[7] Jacqueline L. Beyer, *Integration of Grazing and Crop Agriculture* (Chicago: University of Chicago, Department of Geography research paper, 1957).

sing enterprise may be more effective than traditional public devices in stimulating sustained yield management of eastern forest lands.[8]

These and many other studies indicate we are reaching the stage where systems of social accounting and analysis can reveal the probable social costs and returns from public intervention in resources use. All the measures are rough. Many concentrate upon income effects without reference to change in the resource base. It is paradoxical, however, that at the very time that our economic tools are becoming more precise and more widely applicable, our national thinking has reached a stage at which increasing stress is placed upon aesthetic and national security values which are less susceptible to economic analysis.

It is not possible to sum up all the probable effects of a park plan or a farm improvement scheme in a benefit-cost ratio. Many values defy monetary measurement. Yet there no longer is the excuse of ignorance of method for our failure to make much more refined computations of the impact of an irrigation or power project upon the national economy or to regularly estimate, as Clawson and Held have suggested, the dimensions of the federal land management function.[9] Tools such as benefit-cost analysis can be misused as well as used, and their helpful application requires continuing interest in sharpening them and in asking whether they are employed to justify or to guide a political decision.

Against this background of changing aims and organization for resources conservation and development, and of changing methods of analyzing them, let us turn back to some of the critical questions with which I began, with a view to discovering some of the lines along which further change may be anticipated or perhaps be fostered.

Why have the states generally failed to exercise a strong hand in most fields of resources conservation and development? The role which was envisaged for the states at the Governors' Conference has not been realized. With some happy exceptions they have not exercised strong constructive influence upon the course of reshaping the landscape. Public grazing lands have been widely dissipated and misman-

[8] Roscoe C. Martin, *From Forest to Front Page* (Inter-University Case Program [Birmingham: University of Alabama Press, 1956]).

[9] Marion Clawson and Burnell Held, *The Federal Lands: Their Use and Management* (Baltimore: The Johns Hopkins Press, 1957), pp. 330-33.

aged under state management. Mineral exploitation has been unaffected except as to certain safety measures and in curbing petroleum production to meet demand. Water regulation has been chiefly in the nature of regularizing and protecting private development in a rather rigid pattern.

Some state action, to be sure, has been conspicuously successful in achieving declared conservation aims. The Adirondack preserve in New York has been maintained against all attackers. Forest fire control now is largely a state responsibility, and the federal-state co-operation in forestry supported by interstate compacts in some areas has been encouraging. State water-pollution regulation has grown rapidly in effectiveness, chiefly under the goading of wildlife conservation groups. The licensing of fishing and hunting and the management of fish and game resources have proceeded vigorously. A few state park systems have begun to meet recreational needs.

But the list of successes is short. The one state—California—which had the environment and the plan for comprehensive water development lost the initiative to federal agencies during the emergency public works period, and it seems doubtful that it will recapture the lead.

Why have the states, by and large, not carried more of the responsibility? The sprawling of benefitted areas across state boundaries, the confusing competition among federal agencies, and the enjoyment of federal nonreimbursement programs are no doubt among the reasons. All are factors that make a major extension of state organization extremely difficult. It may be, also, that most states lack the diversity of interest in their political base necessary to cope with strong interest groups, so that only a few can deal with resource problems responsibly. It also may be that state administration flourishes most where federal aims are clearly defined and are administered by one agency. Probably the greatest relative improvement in state activity took place in the Tennessee Valley under the stimulus of one agency. The successful forest fire prevention and wildlife activity lends support to this view.

Can we foresee major extension of state authority? The prospect is not promising.

Why has consolidation of the splintered federal agencies been prevented? The resistance of the major agencies to any consolidation which threatens their administrative integrity and legislative connections is eloquently demonstrated in the relative independence which they now enjoy. The Corps of Engineers, the Forest Service, the Bureau of Reclamation, the Bureau of Mines, and the Soil Conservation Service stand barely shaken by the efforts at partial union. Neither the interest groups supporting them nor the responsible Congressional committees have seen fit to promote consolidation.

Such drastic unions are unlikely to come by public debate; they are more likely to be the product of administrative fiat, as in the case of the Soil Conservation Service-Agricultural Conservation Program merger. But even here disharmonious aims are a chronic deterrent. The concept of multiple-purpose resource management is attractive and easy to support in principle. It runs on the rocks of divisive controversy when efforts are made to reconcile component single purposes. Thus, the Bureau of Reclamation and the Corps of Engineers differ not only in legislative definition of their roles in managing water flow, but in the outlook of supporting interests and Congressional committees. Somewhat similar contrasts are to be found between the Bureau of Land Management and the Forest Service and between the Soil Conservation Service and the Agricultural Stabilization activities. To ascribe these differences to bureaucratic entrenchment or Congressional perversity or to the simple lack of a legislative program is to overlook the basic uncertainty as to the competing public methods to be followed.

From certain administrative points of view there are strong reasons for pushing ahead with consolidation. The question is whether the cost of consolidation would exceed the benefits. Against the advantages of lowered expenses and gains in administrative smoothness, co-operative action, and public appearances, would have to be weighed the disadvantages resulting from administrative inertia and lowered morale, and the possibility that basic cleavages would be submerged rather than reconciled. If such a balance were struck, the scales might be heavily in favor of consolidation, even if the temptation were resisted to favor neat organization charts for their own sake, but I must confess to growing uncertainty as to the outcome in cases where no basic changes in policy accompany the merger.

The same kind of question may be raised as to co-ordination. For while there is a prevailing, benign conviction that agencies working in the same vineyard should co-ordinate their work, it is not clear that the social benefit of such efforts, particularly in peripheral fields, will exceed the costs. As Meyerson and Banfield have pointed out in the housing field, taking account of all possible effects upon other activities may not only be tremendously costly but may paralyze the agency or hold it in a narrow, unimaginative pattern.[10] The point is that there is pitifully little evidence as to the influence of different organizational arrangements upon the landscape and the economy.

Why has the formal co-ordination among federal and federal-state agencies been usually meager? The many efforts at interagency co-ordination either among federal agencies or between federal and state agencies in resources development have yielded a relatively sparse harvest of landscape changes. One of the earlier agents for such collaboration—the National Forest Reservation Commission—shortly became, in effect, a branch of the Forest Service. Federal agency participation in the Federal Power Commission activities became largely perfunctory. Neither the Department of Agriculture nor the Department of the Interior managed to sustain the formal co-ordinating offices which flourished for periods of a few years. The national and drainage basin committee set up by the National Resources Planning Board helped educate their members to deal with more complex issues and prevented much friction which otherwise would have been acute in the burgeoning developments of the thirties. But with the exception of the interagency drainage basin committee, they did not survive agency and Congressional opposition.

While there are many instances of conscientious representatives working together to exchange information and to reduce the intensity and rancor of conflicts stemming from agency rivalry or inconsistent policy, it is difficult to find instances of major new policies or programs which have flowed from those efforts. They may be regarded as facilitating services whose more lasting benefits showed in broadened outlook and co-operative action on the part of numerous members of agency staffs. The marked trend in river basin studies is away from the administrative complexity of joint efforts of the Arkansas-White-

[10] Martin Meyerson and Edwin C. Banfield, *Politics, Planning and the Public Interest* (Glencoe: The Free Press, 1955), pp. 320-22.

Red variety and toward domination by single agencies, as in the current surveys in the Delaware and Potomac basins.

May it be concluded that co-ordination attempts are likely to bear such limited fruit in future? The evidence seems strongly in that direction.

Why has partnership between federal and private enterprise been largely fictional and often exploitive? The concept of "partnership" in resources development is not new; it is as old as the General Dam Act of 1910 and the system of mineral leasing. Its effectiveness has been high in situations where the agreed aim has been to maximize private production of a commodity, such as oil or timber, without regard to auxiliary effects upon other resources. Where other aims are involved, partnership becomes cumbersome, quite aside from the hazards it carries for mismanagement and abuse. Mix grazing with timber or wildlife production and the trouble begins.

In most sectors of resources development the public aims have been established beside rather than as synonymous with private aims of maximizing profit. Only intelligent vigilance prevents unwise contract cutting of national forests or excessive pumpage from oil reserves or single-purpose pre-emption of sites for water storage. Where the interest groups play a strong role in setting regulations, as in the case of local livestock grazers on the public domain, the danger of resource destruction may be great. Present emphasis upon partnership in the water field has the apparent effect of slowing up the investment in public power without stepping up private investment. Perhaps more significant in its long-run implications is the partnership implied in the Watershed Protection Program, where federal investment is matching much smaller private investment for purposes which mix the public effort to save the soil with the private effort to increase income. These projects may in time challenge the one-time pre-eminence of the Rivers and Harbors program in pork-barrel qualities.

My tentative conclusion here is that heightened collaboration between federal and private enterprise does not promise, either in past or present performance, a substantial improvement in the quality of organizational co-operation.

Why have aggressive, articulate interest groups played an increasingly influential role? When the President in 1908 called a pioneering conference he limited the invitation to the key federal agencies and the governors of the states. A similar call today would be more likely to go to the heads of several dozen vigorous interest groups which have full-time representatives in Washington. Those groups have grown markedly in number and strength over the half-century. They were not absent in 1908, but I would venture the observation that their expanding role in the process of decision making has been as momentous as any set of organizational changes in resources conservation and development.

These organized groups now disseminate information, sponsor educational campaigns, advise on management methods, appraise the efforts of individual agencies, and carry the agency battles for appropriations and administrative authority. To a considerable extent they mediate disputes among agencies, and successfully bolster lagging co-ordination. They also work to maintain separate, single-purpose agencies at both state and federal levels.

The wildlife conservation groups are excellent examples. Knowing their own objectives to maintain certain animal populations and habitats, and combining recreational, natural history, and commercial interests, they are organized to carry the fight to the military, the oil men, or the water-management agencies. They sometimes obtain a clear departmental decision where two agencies within the same department may fail.

The proliferation of the interest groups reflects in part a trend which may be observed in other sectors of our political life, but may it not also reflect a movement to fill a vacuum of political power? The conflicts and uncertainties of method inherent in a growing group of single-purpose agencies confronting multiple-purpose aims calls for lively political action to offset the absence of organized means to set new aims and reconcile differences in method.

Taken separately, none of the five questions we have just been considering, nor the various parts of the broader background that preceded them, suggests, upon critical examination, a panacea for the organization of resources conservation and development. We have turned up no sweeping explanations pointing unmistakably to a line of action that would bring wholesale improvements. Consolidation of agencies, co-ordination of both federal and state activities, and improvement of review procedures are often desirable and sometimes attainable, but I am not persuaded that any of these organizational reforms can effect major changes in the impact of public efforts upon the environment as it is now being used or abused. This does not mean that we should stop working for organizational improvements; it means only that we should not be satisfied with those we can get, or feel that if we could get more they would be sufficient in themselves.

Ten years ago I would not have made so guarded a statement. It is only that further experience and reflection have more and more emphasized the durability of social and political facts that outweigh mere neatness and conference-table logic. But what I hope is a more seasoned view is not necessarily a pessimistic one. One practical way of bringing much more order into the prevailing chaos has not as yet been given a real test. It is simply that of broadening the base of political choices on important resource issues. When all of the evidence is reviewed together, rather than in separate pieces, the narrowness of the present base is clearly revealed.

The effectiveness of organization for resources management always will be affected by our stock of ingenuity and courage in making administrative reforms and innovations, and by the flexibility of that system in responding to emerging needs. One of its major limits, however, is in the lack of understanding of national aims and, consequently, of national means as well. So long as this is diffuse we cannot expect any amount of reorganizational legerdemain or budgetary management to more than palliate the difficulties. If we seem confused in the field of defense where there at least seems no doubt that we wish to protect and preserve the United States, how much more complex is the case of natural resources where we are not certain as to what we are to conserve? We are not certain that we want to develop all of our water power or save all of our soil, or how much oil, if any, we should keep under ground, or whether we should curb our appetite for lead in gas and iron in tail fins. Having already and of necessity modified the web of nature, we do not know how far is too far in directing our changes in it.

In recent years we have had a generous review of both policies and administration. Raw materials situations have been assessed; water policy has been proposed; a new attack has been made upon problems of recreation. An important element which has been lacking is a general examination of national aims within the range of politically possible means of achieving them and of the probable impacts of each possible program.

Let me give an example. No area of resources development has been more subject to bitter dispute in recent years than the Upper Colorado. The bloody details of the battle of Echo Park and of the frontier skirmishes along the downstream state lines need not be recounted. A decision was reached by the Congress, as befits all such decisions, in a thoroughly political atmosphere.

That is where and how the decision should be made under our form of government. The instruments of decision making were available: the Congress, the contending federal agencies, an Executive Office and the contentious interest groups. What was lacking was a suitable basis for choice. The basis actually offered was chiefly a plan from the Bureau of Reclamation for development of water for irrigation and electric power, supplemented by critical declarations from other agencies. The analysis offered in support of the plan did not venture an estimate of the probable effects of the irrigation and power development upon the lives and regional organization of the people of the area. It was more narrowly directed toward the reimbursability of the investment and the market for power and irrigation water, recognizing but not attempting to measure the full implications of such outputs for the character and distribution of economic activity. Possible alternatives for use of water, such as in industrial development which might support much greater and more stable population growth, were not examined in detail. There was no broad assessment of the potentialities of the basin for recreational use; rather, attention soon focused upon the threatened impairment of one recreational facility, the Dinosaur National Monument. There still was no comprehensive appraisal of the needs to improve the agricultural productive plant of the nation and of the relative effectiveness of the many means, including irrigation, to such improvement. Nor, in fact, were there any estimates of the consequences of possible alternative choices for public investment in land, water, minerals, and transport in the Upper Colorado.

As the Upper Colorado plan was presented to the Congress the choice was essentially to accept it, to accept it with reservations, or to reject it. Those who endorsed it had no grounds for assurance that it was the most effective means for stimulating development of the area's resources in the public interest, loosely defined. They only knew that it was the sole detailed plan available and that their choice was between the Upper Colorado plan or nothing for a considerable time to come.

The Upper Colorado experience is symptomatic of a large proportion of the decisions made on both the national and the state levels concerning natural resources. A program or policy growing out of the relatively circumscribed task of one agency is put forward for approval or rejection. It is accepted, accepted with modifications, or rejected. The two fundamental questions of what will be its full effects and what would be the effects of other possible programs cannot be answered with the data and time then available.

The kind of analysis the nation most needs would present estimates of the consequences of each of the politically practicable lines of public action. Thereby, the political process of choice would be sharpened rather than curbed, and governmental intervention seen in perspective with the alternatives.

An organization or procedure to sharpen the process of political choice has not yet had a fair trial in the United States. Ephemeral commissions are a lame substitute. The task never was undertaken at the state level, and at the national level in the National Resources Planning Board it was loaded with public works review and had barely begun before it was halted. Moreover, the tools for analysis were much less promising fifteen years ago than they are today. The Bureau of the Budget has tended to stop short of exploring viable alternatives, although it has made efforts, as in the case of water programs, to establish criteria which would permit comparison. New machinery is needed to carry out a more penetrating appraisal in the Executive Office and in the departments.

Agency consolidation, policy formulation, Congressional reorganization, and interagency co-ordination may, indeed, help reduce friction and reconcile operating methods. But they are less basic than an agency or procedure to focus attention upon the choices and effects of public action. Even with such a mechanism we could expect continued conflict, divergence, and pluralism of approach. As Norman

Wengert has stated, we should welcome such indecision and friction so far as they reflect searching and experimenting with promising lines of action. We should be dissatisfied only when the choices are not made from the full range that could be marshalled with our potentially available stock of knowledge and skills.

The conclusion may be applied to the water resources situation and remedies with which we began. In terms of maximizing public returns from public investments and of achieving the intended results with minimum delays, there is need to improve the organization for planning, construction, and operation of river basin works for multiple purposes. Most of the remedies which have been suggested, short of wholesale unification of policy, would offer only slight hope of improvement so long as the basis for choosing among possible river basin programs and their alternatives is limited to the proposals that the agencies are expected to produce under existing law. Organized efforts to appraise the choices and their effects before programs reach the budget stage would help set the criteria and widen the basis for choice. It also would permit more reasonable decision as to what programs should be adopted, and as to the efficacy of different organizational arrangements to carry them out. Controversy would be heightened, agency reorganization would be stimulated, and interest groups would be given new ammunition and fresh perspectives. Participation—both financial and administrative—by state and local agencies would become more practicable. I find it difficult to imagine any circumstances in which a Missouri or Upper Colorado basin commitment would be simply abandoned because it was judged unsound; more likely is its being replaced by a constructive alternative which promised wider and more lasting benefits.

Assessment of effects of not only one resource development program but a number of multiple-purpose programs would require drastic changes in present procedures. But several current factors are creating a more favorable climate for some such effort at appraisal.

One is the pressure of urban activity and population on the land. The second is the prospect for shortages in various sectors of material supply in our country. The third is the hard fact that as our income increases in the United States the gap between our income and the income per capita of most other countries in the world is widening rather than narrowing, and therefore our responsibility for offering some continued aid and assistance to these countries is likely to increase and will not change with any decrease in our own reserves or resources.

For these reasons there is the hope and the possibility that the American people will move to use the best tools at their command for a studied, balanced appraisal at the national level of the effects of alternative resource programs and projects.

Whether or not the federal government recognizes a greatly refined appraisal process as an aid to decision making, nonfederal agencies will be needed for that purpose, to double on a small scale for such action in its absence, or to give it vigorous competition in its functioning. The research program of Resources for the Future is a valuable service in that direction. It demonstrates analysis which should be practiced and refined on a large scale, it reminds us of the tremendous complexity of such an operation, and it directs attention to the unfolding challenges.

Of the numerous organizational changes that may be in order, none seem more promising of benefits to the whole process of preserving or reforming the American landscape than those which promote a continuing appraisal of the probable results of following the choices which are open.

NOTE   In preparing this paper frequent reference has been made to a number of studies of resources administration among which the more valuable are here listed. Grateful acknowledgment is made for the ideas in them, but specific references have not been given except where there is direct quotation.

James W. Fesler, "National Water Resources Administration," *Law and Contemporary Problems,* XXII (1957), 444-71.

Charles M. Hardin, *The Politics of Agriculture* (Glencoe: The Free Press, 1952).

Henry C. Hart, *The Dark Missouri* (Madison: University of Wisconsin Press, 1957).

Albert Lepawsky, *State Planning and Economic Development in the South* (Washington: National Planning Association, 1949).

Charles McKinley, *Uncle Sam in the Pacific Northwest* (Berkeley: University of California Press, 1952).

R. G. Tugwell and E. C. Banfield, "Governmental Planning at Mid-century," *Journal of Politics,* 13 (1951), 133-63.

Norman Wengert, *Natural Resources and the Political Struggle* (Garden City: Doubleday and Company, Inc., 1955).

The author is indebted to Edwin C. Banfield, William L. Frederick, and Page L. Ingraham for critical suggestions during the preparation of this paper.

CAN WE STILL AFFORD A
SEPARATE RESOURCES POLICY?

✍ *Charles M. Hardin*

Gilbert White's major conclusion is that the United States needs a much more systematic method for comparative evaluation of resource programs, especially in the fields of land and water. I fully agree with this proposal. Its adoption would make our natural resource policy choices much clearer and sharper. I do not think, however, that Mr. White goes nearly far enough. After weighing the various kinds of resources projects against each other, we need some governmental means for taking the whole field of natural resources as a policy area, and subjecting *it* to vigorous comparative evaluation with the other large areas of national policy.

We need to improve our ways of doing things politically so that the aims of policies may be better understood, the means evaluated more

---

CHARLES M. HARDIN, Professor of Political Science at the University of Chicago, has taught at Harvard University (1940–45) and has lectured widely among United States universities, particularly on his research specialty which embraces public policy in agriculture and in natural resources, on which he has published numerous articles, and two books, *The Politics of Agriculture: Soil Conservation and the Struggle for Power in Rural America* and *Freedom in Agricultural Education*. He has acted as a consultant to the Department of Agriculture, to the Tennessee Valley Authority, and to the Agricultural Extension Committee on Public Policy. In 1957 he had a Rockefeller Grant for the study of agricultural policy and politics in Latin America. Born in Lander, Wyoming, in 1908, Mr. Hardin has a B.A. from the University of Wyoming, an M.A. from the University of Colorado, and a Ph.D. from Harvard University.

227

effectively, and the choices among policies subjected to more searching comparisons. To this end we need major political changes which,
in themselves, entail some risks but which should be undertaken because in our radically worsened international position the risks of
doing nothing are much greater. The supporting reasons, long persuasive, became overwhelming with the drastic adverse shift in world
political power that crystallized late in 1957. But there is, of course,
no assurance that we shall listen to reason.

Professor White wants new machinery in the Executive Office itself
and in the departments. The near unanimity of natural resource policy
critics in proposing to suspend the fist of the President over the programs and agencies involved shows how formidable the difficulties of
co-ordination are perceived to be. But there are two things wrong
with this approach.

First, these proposals are largely confined to improving relationships among the major land and water agencies in their central development programs; but the times call for a much more systematic cross-
evaluation of natural resource policies both internally and also in
their relationships to other policies, especially to fiscal and foreign
policies. Until quite recently it seemed that we might wisely try to
separate from the general stream of policy development the decisions
on public land and water programs, in order to improve their comparative evaluation, say in the President's Office. Now we need to
organize and develop all our resources if we are to survive the long
future of deadly international competition. We must balance expenditures for natural resource development against other financial claimants, national defense, for example, or education. This never has been
absolutely necessary before. Moreover, we need to weigh natural resource policy as a whole including the present and future availability
of various minerals which, despite the miracles of substitution, are still
essential to our economy but which are also in short (or even non-
existent) domestic supply.[1]

Finally, our continued national survival now clearly lies in integrating our economy as completely and as rapidly as possible with
the economies of our allies and friendly nations. Many of these na-

[1] See a series of articles by Richard Rutter upon "The Dangerous Decline of
U.S. Natural Resources," *New York Times,* November 9-12, 1957.

tions supply minerals in competition with our domestic producers; many export agricultural products of which we also have current surpluses. Economic integration with such countries will be attained only by overcoming grinding conflicts of interests of which many are entrenched in our natural resource policy—some of these policies, such as petroleum and wool quotas and tariffs on lead and zinc, running obviously and directly counter to integration; and others having a more indirect though probably no less powerful adverse effect through a series of apparent deals or logrolls, for example, between reclamation and sugar interests. We have lived for a long time with these political bargains which have been rationalized as the price of union. With dramatic suddenness the bargains have become dangerous and the apologies obsolete.

The second weakness of current proposals for reform lies in the assumption that the problem will be solved if it is left in a basket on the President's doorstep. When the problem is seen in proper breadth and perspective, however, the logical place for the evaluation required is in the Bureau of the Budget. The Bureau now is responsible for legislative, fiscal, and administrative overview; it is already a part of the Office of the President. Nothing is gained by trying to shove decisions closer to the President himself. F. D. Roosevelt's defeats at the hands of the Army Engineers in the Kings River project and (in part) of the Forest Service in the reorganization bill of 1938 show that even an extremely powerful and vigorous president may not be able to control natural resource interests. If the Presidency can be given stronger and more continuous power over the substance of policy, over finances, and over administration, then the Bureau of the Budget can do the staff work necessary for formulating Presidential decisions. If not, then not even the President can do the job effectively.

The major disagreement with my analysis is stated by Ernest S. Griffith who argues in the opening essay of this book that our political institutions are now properly organized for making natural resource policy, needing only to improve and to make better use of present instruments (chiefly staff services) for organizing intelligence. "In minor matters," he says, administrative and legislative, local or special interests may prevail; in the great landmarks in forest, power, land, river development, mines, the public interest has usually prevailed—but it has prevailed in great measure by taking into account the vitality and the social contribution of the private interests.

This position, widely shared among political scientists, was defensible until the radical shift in our power position became clear late in 1957. Even before then many of our natural resource policies were properly criticized. At a median cost of $504 per acre, the Missouri Valley development program planned to irrigate an additional 5 million acres, of which 10 per cent would produce sugar beets and thus account for 31 per cent of the expected benefits cited to justify the expenditure. Yet every additional pound of sugar beets so produced would have to be protected by a quota and subsidized by the government! [2] Such outlays are sometimes justified as redistributions of income. In that event it would be useful to know who is benefitted. Under the Agricultural Conservation Program, now in its twenty-second year, I estimated a few years ago that 20 per cent of the farmers were getting about 60 per cent of the payment. Under the price support programs the USDA calculated in December of 1957 that 27 per cent of the farmers got 79 per cent of the benefits.[3] None of these concentrations of benefits would appear remotely to approach those that arise from the depletion allowance in petroleum. Nevertheless, only a few years ago we could seemingly afford it all. Our mobile, expanding, fully employed economy encouraged the private pursuit of opportunity and permitted a levelling-up in the general community, so long as we could maintain a semi-detached state from the rest of the world and hence consider our foremost problems to be essentially domestic ones.

[2] Edward F. Renshaw, *Toward Responsible Government* (Chicago: Idyia Press, 1957), pp. 12, 22, 24. The projected increase in domestic sugar beet acreage would require an amendment to the Sugar Act considerably to increase the U.S. share of the domestic sugar market.

[3] Charles M. Hardin, *The Politics of Agriculture* (Glencoe: The Free Press, 1952), p. 109. USDA 3647-57 (December 10, 1957). Edward F. Renshaw has made a similar calculation using 1946 figures: that some 30 per cent of the farms got 80 per cent of the price support benefits (forthcoming paper, "A Note on Farm Price Support Programs," Department of Economics, University of Chicago, 1958).

My belief now is that we can no longer live with these lavish and indiscriminate policies. We must re-examine the cost of heavy spending programs in natural resources, in agriculture, and elsewhere. We must reassess these policies as they substantially affect our ability to integrate our economy internationally. In addition, although some economists appear to believe that we can substitute ourselves out of nearly any natural resource shortage, we appear to need a much sharper, and continuous, appraisal of the availability and use of critical resources. For these reasons a much more systematic and comparative review and evaluation of natural resource and other policies is required.

At present the big natural resource programs secure their budgetary millions, acquire their field administrations, cement their Congressional friendships, and join hands with well-heeled interest groups which have formed (often with their own assistance) around their programs. Many internal struggles have occurred—Agriculture *vs.* Interior, Army Engineers *vs.* Reclamation, Soil Conservation Service *vs.* Tennessee Valley Authority—but such contests have been to control larger chunks of the budget rather than to whittle it down or, more significantly in our present situation, to compel a comparative evaluation of spending in different areas and for different purposes. Indeed, the big programs in this area seem more and more to be added together, escorted politely but firmly through the Bureau of the Budget, and paraded by the genial Appropriations Committees to the Treasury (with a courtesy call for the President's signature). These programs may get knocked down a few millions occasionally, but they are too powerful politically to have to undergo thorough comparative examinations. In addition, I believe that support of the big-spending natural resource programs is obtained by a series of deals which involve restrictions on imports and subsidies for exports. I refer specifically to the quotas and restrictions, present or proposed, some of them directly in the natural resource field (petroleum, lead and zinc) and some of them outside the natural resource field proper like quotas on Japanese textiles—but all of them, I think, knit together politically in a series of logrolls which we can no longer safely endure.

I conclude then that Gilbert White's proposed reform should logically be extended to include the comparative evaluation of all our

natural resource policies and their reconciliation with fiscal and foreign policies. To realize this will require a major governmental reorganization such as Arthur Smithies has proposed in his study of *The
Budgetary Process in the United States.*[4] On the President's side alone,
Smithies' proposals involve the Bureau of the Budget, the National
Security Council, the Council of Economic Advisers, and the Treasury. Moreover, his sweeping procedural reforms, as he recognizes, will
be unavailing unless the prestige of the Bureau of the Budget can be
greatly enhanced so that men will not place a higher value on being
undersecretary of the Treasury or of State or vice-president of the
International Bank than they do on being Director of the Budget. Yet
even Smithies does not make it clear that his reforms really depend
for their success upon fundamental political change (the need and
hence, perhaps, the possibility for which were not so clear when he
wrote).

The nature and extent of the necessary political changes are suggested by Samuel H. Beer's analysis of British *Treasury Control.*[5] "In
American government [Beer writes] there is nothing really comparable to the most important form of treasury control, the requirement of
prior approval." He refers to a governmental process which authori-
tatively weighs the claims of public health against those of agriculture,
of education against transportation, of defense against social services.
In his final chapter, Beer tries to explain why Treasury control is
effective. He cites a number of reasons: the standards of the civil
service, the effect of the plural executive, and the authority of the
Chancellor of the Exchequer. The last two clearly imply that disci-
plined agreements are reached, based upon a concert of power within
the government. Without this Britain could not achieve Treasury control, and without something like it we will not attain its equivalent.

[4] New York: McGraw-Hill, 1955, esp. Chap. X.
[5] Oxford University, England (Clarendon Press, 1957).

THE PLUS SIDE OF THE RECORD

Robert E. Merriam

Gilbert White's thought-provoking analysis of the difficulties involved in organizing effectively for the development and management of our natural resources makes it easy to see why many people feel that we have not made much progress in solving such stubborn problems. Appropriately, he has focused attention on water resources, since this area involves perhaps the most sensitive and complex organizational issues in the natural resource field. Certainly there still is much room for improvement. But that should not lead us to overlook the progress that has been made over the years: we have substantially improved our organizational structure and have developed more effective procedures for the review, selection, and co-ordination of water and re-

---

R O B E R T E. M E R R I A M , Deputy Director of the Bureau of the Budget since March 1958, was for eighteen months prior to his appointment Assistant Director, with supervision over the labor and welfare and resources areas of the Bureau's activities. His earlier federal service, as assistant to the Deputy Administrator of the National Housing Agency in 1941–42, was broken by three years of war service, after which he entered the field of city administration and politics, first in 1946–47 as Director of the Metropolitan Housing Council in Chicago, and then from 1947 to 1955 as alderman for the city of Chicago. In this capacity he chaired the city's committee on housing and its emergency committee on crime. In 1955 he ran as Republican candidate for mayor of Chicago. Mr. Merriam is the author of *Dark December: The Full Account of the Battle of the Bulge,* and is co-author of *The American Government: Democracy in Action,* and of *Going Into Action.* He was born in Chicago in 1918; received his M.A. from the University of Chicago in 1940.

lated land resource projects. If much remains to be accomplished, let us acknowledge also that much worthwhile work has been done. Let me point out as examples some of the steps that have been taken towards organizing for more effective planning, co-ordination, and execution of water resource programs.

An Executive Order (Number 9384), issued in 1943, provided a focus in the Bureau of the Budget for the orderly review and co-ordination of all public works projects originating within the Executive Branch, including, of course, water resource projects.

Also in 1943, the Federal Inter-Agency River Basin Committee was established by informal agreement among the Bureau of Reclamation, the Army Engineers, the Department of Agriculture, and the Federal Power Commission. Later, the Department of Commerce, the Federal Security Agency (now the Department of Health, Education, and Welfare), and the Department of Labor joined the committee. Through the committee, the federal agencies were able to co-operate more fully in the preparation of reports on multiple-purpose water resource projects and to correlate their planning efforts. It operated through notification of investigations, and the free exchange of data and of advice concerning the participation of each agency. The committee also sponsored several technical subcommittees. The so-called "Green Book," prepared by a subcommittee on benefits and costs in May of 1950, is recognized by the resource agencies as a useful guide for economic analyses of river basin projects.

The effectiveness of the Federal Inter-Agency River Basin Committee was limited in that it was a voluntary group which operated on the basis of the unanimous consent of its members. Moreover, it did not have official recognition from either the Executive Office or the Congress. To correct these deficiencies, and to take better advantage of the usefulness of the committee approach, the Inter-Agency Committee on Water Resources was approved by President Eisenhower on May 26, 1954. This committee enjoys formal recognition and support by the Cabinet officers concerned and has the backing of the President. In addition, its operations have been improved by minimizing procedural and administrative matters in order to free the time of the principals for matters of broader interest.

The purpose of the Inter-Agency Committee is substantially similar to that of its predecessor committee, namely, to provide a mechanism for the co-ordination of policies, programs, and activities of the federal departments and agencies working in the field of water and related land resources. It also undertakes the resolution of interagency differences, and has authority to suggest to the President such changes in law or policy as seem necessary or desirable.

The committee has chartered regional interagency committees for the Columbia Basin, the Missouri Basin, the Pacific Southwest, and Arkansas-White-Red Basin and the New York-New England area, all of which had been operating previously under various administrative arrangements. Since the affected states are represented on each of these field committees, an opportunity is provided for a co-ordinated state, local, and federal approach to the water resource problems of these major drainage systems.

In December 1952, the Bureau of the Budget took a further step toward the development of uniform standards and criteria for the selection of the most needed and worthwhile projects proposed by Executive agencies by issuing its widely known Circular A-47. Although this circular cannot, nor is it intended to, modify any provisions of law, it serves as a useful yardstick, and establishes a standard for Executive review of water resource projects proposed by federal agencies. I must add, however, that even this rather modest step has not met with great enthusiasm from the Congress.

In addition, I should mention the useful function played by a number of *ad hoc* committees such as the one now preparing a plan for the full development of the water resources of the Delaware Basin. There are also continuing study groups, in the Executive Branch and elsewhere, which provide useful information on the intricate and controversial problems involved in attempting to assure the most effective development of our nation's water and related land resources. Thus, while we admittedly have a long way to go, we also can look with some satisfaction on our progress to date.

What about prospects for further progress?

Mr. White has noted some of the difficulties that have blocked attempts to bring about agency consolidations or to set up arrangements for the review and co-ordination of resources programs and projects. During the past several years I have had an opportunity to learn at first hand of the agonizing frustrations which face one attempting to act in this area. I am alternately impressed and depressed by what I see. I am impressed by the caliber of the personnel involved, their dedication to duty, their fund of knowledge, their imagination in their professional spheres. I am depressed at the amount of time one has to spend at the federal level in ironing out differences of opinion among these various groups of highly dedicated people. A recent example of the frustrations I am thinking of is the long, unfinished sequel to the report of the Presidential Advisory Committee on Water Resources Policy which President Eisenhower established in 1954. In December 1955, the committee submitted its report to the President, who commended its purposes and objectives and recommended that the Congress give prompt attention to its proposals.

The report contained four important organizational recommendations: (1) that a co-ordinator of water resources be established in the Executive Office of the President to provide a focal point for policy and program development; (2) that a three-member board of review be created in the Executive Office of the President to provide objective advice on the engineering and economic feasibility of proposed projects; (3) that a permanent interagency committee on water resources be constituted under the chairmanship of the co-ordinator of water resources; and (4) that regional or river basin water resources committees be set up, consisting of federal and state representatives and headed by independent chairmen appointed by the President. It was contemplated that the various federal and state agencies could work together to co-ordinate water and related land resource planning and development activities, prepare comprehensive plans, and submit annual work schedules.

The four recommendations relating to organization were the product of careful consideration on the part of the committee members and their expert staffs. However, issuance of the report brought forth immediate criticism of the recommendations, both from key Congressional figures and various interest groups. The proposal for a co-ordinator of water resources led to special outcries, the contention being that the co-ordinator could become a "czar," capable of running roughshod over agencies charged with administering specific programs. The proposed board of review was similarly challenged. It soon became painfully apparent that the possibility of Congressional approval of these two proposals was indeed remote. This experience certainly underlines Mr. White's comment that we seem to have no national approach to our resource development programs. It demonstrates to me, at least, that we have a long way to go before we develop any such consensus.

The President's Committee also recommended establishment of regional water resources committees. While no cure-all, such an action, by assigning the planning job to adequately equipped regional groups with full state participation, would represent an important step towards the efficient development of our national land and water resources.

The matter of state participation is of particular importance. Mr. White asks why the states have not taken a stronger role in natural resource development, and mentions a number of factors that have tended to inhibit state action. I agree with the main lines of his analysis, particularly in regard to the inhibiting effects of the federal government's eagerness to foot the whole bill; the dollars that come from Washington somehow look easier to come by than those from closer to home. Yet we should note that state expenditures for natural resource developments have nearly quadrupled since the end of the war, compared to a little over a doubling in federal expenditures for the same purposes. Given proper encouragement, I believe that the states can and will take an increasingly important part in the vast job of developing the natural resources of this nation.

The size of the over-all task underlines the importance and necessity of co-operative participation by federal, state, local, and private interests. No single interest can hope to do it all—or even a major portion of it—adequately. For example, a recent estimate by The Brookings Institution indicates that a capital outlay of over 70 billion dollars will be needed over the next several decades for natural resource programs other than power. The Federal Power Commission estimates that by 1980 we will require three times the installed generating capacity that we now have, a requirement of another 100 billion dollars. Clearly the federal government cannot do all or even a large part of either of these jobs, although there are many areas in which the federal government must have a major responsibility. This is especially true in those water resources projects which because of their size and complexity are obviously beyond the means of state or local groups. But the role of the federal government in the conservation and development of our natural resources should be shaped to encourage rather than displace the necessary efforts of state, local, and private groups.

I am surprised by Mr. White's statement that "present emphasis upon partnership in the water field has the apparent effect of slowing up the investment in public power without stepping up private investment." During the last five years, 9.9 million kilowatts of new capacity were installed at federal plants compared with 4.7 million during the five years before then. The difference in growth of national capacity is also striking: 42.3 million kilowatts in the last five years compared with 29.9 in the previous period. The policy of encouraging state, local, and private interests to develop hydro sites, which is the most discussed aspect of the partnership principle, has been an important factor in this increase. In the four-year period ending June 1953, installed hydroelectric capacity under Federal Power Commission licenses had increased by only 2.8 million kilowatts, and planned ultimate capacity had increased by the same amount. Contrast that with the four years ending June 1957, in which time installed capacity under FPC licenses increased 6.3 million kilowatts, and ultimate capacity, 8.4 million kilowatts. I might add that the first partnership developments occurred in Theodore Roosevelt's administration; and between 1906 and 1953 some twenty-six so-called partnership projects were constructed in thirteen states, twelve of these being under Republican administrations and fourteen in Democratic administrations.

The job of developing our natural resources is one of immense proportions; it involves problems that are varied and widespread, and that differ according to local and regional conditions. To assure adaptability and responsiveness to local needs, we must provide better co-ordination at regional levels with strong local participation and enlightened backing by the national Administration and the Congress. This co-operative approach will not be any easier than other truly democratic processes. But I believe it is the approach most likely to contribute to what both Mr. White and I agree is necessary—a sharpening of the process of political choice, and a perspective in which governmental intervention can be compared with alternatives. Most of all, we need to develop the kind of perspective which can transcend and override the prevailing concept of competing, often conflicting, single-purpose or limited-objective programs.

THE FEDERAL RESPONSIBILITY
FOR LEADERSHIP

William Pincus

Gilbert White's plea for a broader basis for selecting resource programs and policies highlights the need for a clear presentation for public consideration of the choices and possible alternatives in conservation and development. The more confused an area of public policy and action, the less likelihood there is that the citizenry will have the foundation for the intelligent choices which make democracy work for the greatest good of the greatest number.

To make the field of resources development meaningful, in terms of responsibility to the widest segments of the population, is an especially challenging area of public policy. Without special efforts, it is not immediately apparent to the public how resources conservation and development activities involve most human beings. The resources area is not the only area of public activity which seems esoteric in this regard. There are others, such as money and banking. But many

---

WILLIAM PINCUS for over a year has been with the public affairs program of The Ford Foundation. His previous work has been in government administration, particularly in government administration of resources. Most recently he was Associate General Counsel to the House Committee on Government Operations; from 1951 to 1954 he was Assistant Director of the Bureau of Land Management; and for several years prior to that was with the Bureau of the Budget. He has also served with both the Hoover commissions. Mr. Pincus was born at Philadelphia, Pa., in 1920. He obtained his degree in government from Brooklyn College and holds an LL.B. from George Washington University.

areas of government are relatively easy for the average citizen to comprehend in the terms in which he usually comprehends: How will this or that affect people, including myself? The functions of the Federal Security Agency are a good, clear example of this. Just look around the federal government and one can find a multitude of others. Even agriculture has largely been treated as a human clientele matter and part of our pains in agricultural policy today are due to the conflicts between increasing impersonalization of more industrialized farming and the older approach of the situation of people making a living on the land.

State and local government show the same characteristics. Education is something we think we all understand and want to participate in. The administration of criminal law and psychology, narcotics, alcoholism, family relations, juvenile delinquency are in the darker recesses of the public policy area, not because we are not involved, but because we don't like to feel that we are involved. We shove these problems aside. We sweep them under the rug. We refuse to accept the fact that these involve us. The result is slow and extremely difficult progress, and indeed even retrogression at times.

The lesson seems clear to me—an activity must give our citizens a sense of involvement. Its meaning must be translatable into terms of importance for them before we get the fullest citizen attention and ultimately the kinds of searching public scrutiny, debate, conflict, and finally the resolution of issues into tangible public policy and action to the benefit of the greatest number.

Now what has this got to do with organizational co-operation for resources conservation and development? It has this relationship: unless we do something to pull together organizational responsibilities for resources development, there will be no clear picture presented to the public for a determination among alternative choices. The people will never feel involved in something which is so fragmented that they cannot possibly understand. Even names are important in conveying a sense of content of program. In this regard we are more deficient at the federal level than at the state level. While we experts analyze and discuss "resources," and "conservation," and "development," these terms seldom appear in the official organizational titles involved.

The key problem is breadth of participation, not of whether we agree or disagree with minorities that get their hands on the controls. It is just as unhealthy for a democracy to have public policy too largely influenced by small groups of self-appointed saviors and guardians as it is to have such policy disproportionately determined by small groups directly interested economically in resources development. Each of these groups has a necessary contribution to make, but the real test of progress in our attention as a nation to resources conservation and development is the extent to which we can succeed in involving larger groups of the population in this important area of public policy.

There is a recent tendency to go along tacitly with the organizational confusion and increasing overlapping which has characterized efforts at resources conservation and development over the years. This is alarming. There is too much of an acceptance of our long-standing troubles in the resources field that result from lack of organizational soundness. I sense some of this in Mr. White's paper.

Without some fundamental reorganization there can be no basis for intelligent national policy, for involvement of the public at large, and for fixing responsibility in a democracy as it needs to be fixed.

The creation of the Department of Defense has not solved the problem of organization for national defense. But it has at least provided a start for making some of the most important choices clearer. We may not have been able to identify all the choices clearly enough and some decisions may have been questionable, but I don't think that most people would advocate a return to the previous situation as a solution to our problems.

Yet, at the federal level, we have actually done little to rationalize the growing but scattered resources functions in water, land, minerals, etc.

In water resources, we have actually retrogressed from the achievements of 1920, when the Federal Power Act became law. From an interagency committee designed to co-ordinate river basin development, the Federal Power Commission was later converted to a regulatory and planning agency. I know that there were reasons for the change about ten years later, but the fact remains that little has been done to pick up the threads and go forward. Some moves were made to broaden the base of the Interior Department by moving some additional resources functions into the Department and by taking less related functions out in the late thirties and in the forties. But the Department remains basically a western department, with the major citizen interest being shown by those who directly exploit the resources, and, on the other side, by self-appointed guardians of the public interest—the so-called conservationists who represent a minute fraction of the population. I could go on to talk about specialized clienteles of the Army Corps of Engineers, the Forest Service, the Soil Conservation Service and other agencies.

The only successful experiment in making resources development meaningful to all the people of a region has taken place in the Tennessee Valley. And this is not because it has been done through a valley authority. It is because the over-all responsibility for resources development was placed under one roof so that the total dimensions of the job could be perceived by the people to the point where most of them felt involved. This is what we need on the national scene: a national organization, agency, or department which will be able to bring together enough of the basic resources functions so that its plans, ambitions, and actions will seem important and meaningful to all the people. Our democracy can actually be revitalized by such an organizational change. Our form of government is not operating on all its cylinders when persons in the large urban centers in all parts of the country and when the whole population of the East feel little or no involvement in major resources conservation and development controversies. It is deeply disturbing when so many votes in Congress on such important matters are not directly on the merits of the issues because the constituents back home have so little concern with these problems.

We need a department of resources development at the national level, which will be responsible to all the people and which can help the people and the Congress understand the issues and the challenges and present them with choices for intelligent discussion. This is an old idea, but the need for some such improvement is greater than ever. The need will not be superseded by any number of ancillary committees for co-ordinating purposes or by any superstructure of expert analyzers and reviewers at the Presidential level—as attractive as such things may be.

As to the role of state and local government, and more particularly of the people at the local level, I don't think there is any particular magic in nonfederal government as such; all virtue doesn't reside there. It is more important to use the vitality of our citizens than to joust with the theologies of different levels of government. In this regard, we have learned much in the last twenty-five years about organizing citizens' energies at the local level. Soil conservation districts, the TVA, and other devices have shown some of the possibilities. With better organization at the federal level, the role of private citizens and private industry at the local level will be strengthened. Today it is being dissipated in a myriad of organizations and efforts, vainly attempting to cope with the frustrations imposed by a multiplicity of federal and state agencies. The energies of the people are being wasted in this area because of the irrationality of governmental organization in the resources area. Proper federal organization, and that alone, can make clearer the role of the states, of the local organizations of citizens, and of private industry. We have the knowledge and experience in other areas of public policy. It is time to apply the lessons we have learned in the resources area.

The lesson of our whole history of development as a nation is that state, local, and private initiative cannot substitute for that part of leadership which must come from the federal level. Interstate compacts and individual state efforts have unique and invaluable contributions to make, but to argue that these are the road to a national resources program of meaningful content to all our citizens is like arguing that our people could have developed their part of the continent under the Articles of Confederation just as well as they did under the Constitution. Poor organization at the national level frustrates organizational co-operation by all levels of government and by private enterprise. The answer is to strive for improved organization at the national level in order to strengthen citizen participation below and not to be led into thinking that we can go ahead as we need to in resources development without adequate federal organization and leadership.

The responsibility for leadership is basically that of the federal government. If it sets its house in order, it will be possible to perceive for the first time how state, local, and private efforts can join in a true partnership for resources conservation and development involving all the people. We cannot have true organizational co-operation without the central reform of the federal government. Not any superstructure at the Presidential level, nor any conglomeration of organizational devices below the federal level, can make up for this deficiency. And the basic drive for progress must come from the people. Such a liberation and kindling of their energies must come from the interest and involvement furnished by a national leadership for resources development.

INDEX

AAAS. *See* American Association for the Advancement of Science
Ackerman, Edward A., 118*n*
Adirondack Mountains, 17; forest fire, 68
Agricultural Adjustment Acts (1933, 1938), 13
Agricultural Bill (1907), 6
Agricultural Conservation Program, 230
Agricultural Entry Act (1914), 9
Agricultural Experiment Stations, research activities of, 63
Agricultural Extension Service, 20
Agriculture:
crop production, 62–63, 67–69;
expenditures for, 230–31;
external economies, value of private action in, 174;
livestock production, 69;
price support benefits, farmers' share in, 230, 230*n*;
raw materials, supply inelasticities of, 169;
research in, 63, 65;
and soil classification, 63–64;
see also Irrigation; Land use; Soil conservation
Albright, Horace M., xi
Allegheny River, 129
Allin, Bushrod W., 196*n*, 201*n*
American Association for the Advancement of Science, 25, 26
American Forestry Association, 25, 26
Arizona, copper deposits in, 57
Arkansas-White-Red Basin, 218–19, 235
Asia: population growth in, 130; urbanization in, 127
Atomic Energy Act (1946), 17
Automobile production, 104; and competition, 99; and consumer demand, 94

Ballinger, Richard A., 8, 42
Ballinger-Pinchot controversy, 42, 43, 44
Banfield, Edwin C., 214*n*, 218, 218*n*, 226*n*
Bannerman, H. M., 49*n*
Barton, P. B., Jr., 57, 57*n*
Bauer, P. T., 170*n*
Beer, Samuel H., 232
Belgian Congo, uranium deposits in, 58
Benefit-cost analysis, 215
Bennett, Hugh, 23, 197
Beyer, Jacqueline L., 214*n*
Bituminous Coal Act (1935), 15
Blanchard, Newton C., 53*n*
Board of Economic Warfare, 37
Bogue, D. J., 122*n*
Bowaters Southern Paper Corporation, 214
Bowers, Edward A., 26
Brady, Dorothy S., 122*n*
Brandywine Creek, Delaware, sediment control in, 64
Bronk, Detlev W., 143, 143*n*
Brookings Institution, The, 237
Brown, Harrison, 102, 107, 108
Budgetary Process in the United States, The, 232
Bureau of American Ethnology, 5*n*
Bureau of the Budget, 11, 20, 223, 231, 232; Circular A–47, issuance of, 235; review of public works projects by, 234; role of, in evaluation of resource policy, 229
Bureau of the Census, U.S. population projections of, 101
Bureau of Forestry, 160
Bureau of Land Management, 217
Bureau of Mines, 7, 217
Bureau of Reclamation, 217, 222, 231, 234
Burke, Edmund, 73

247

The Library of Congress has cataloged this book as follows:

Resources for the Future.

Perspectives on conservation; essays on America's natural resources, by John Kenneth Galbraith ₁and others₁ Edited by Henry Jarrett.   Baltimore, Johns Hopkins Press ₁1958₁

260 p.   24 cm.

1. Natural resources—U. S.
ɪɪ. Jarrett, Henry, ed.   ɪɪɪ. Title.

ɪ. Galbraith, John Kenneth, 1908–

HC103.7.R46   333.72   58–59888 ‡

Library of Congress